MY LITTLE
RED SCHOOLHOUSE

MY LITTLE
RED SCHOOLHOUSE

By

Harley A. Henderson

DORRANCE & COMPANY
Philadelphia

FOREWORD

While none of the specific events in *My Little Red Schoolhouse* are true, they all must have occurred or at least have happened in a very similar way, to some rural teacher somewhere. My book is based on broad truths, and on my experience as a teacher, minister, counselor, and companion to children over more years than I care to admit.

The book is set in the central part of the United States only because I am more familiar with the geography of that region. The story could have taken place in almost any rural school from the Atlantic to the Pacific.

CONTENTS

MY LITTLE
RED SCHOOLHOUSE

CHAPTER I

MY TEACHING DEBUT

I didn't plan to be a schoolteacher. From early teens I dreamed of the ministry. To stand in a great cathedral and stir the multitudes by the beauty and power of flowery phrases was my highest aspiration. I was an extrovert with a rich baritone voice, short, plump physique, and a spreading middle, so, except for height, I seemed destined to ministerial success.

The ministry, plus a wife, became a reality but the great cathedral never materialized. I struggled to keep threadbare suits presentable for Sunday morning services, which gave little glamour to the canonical paunch that developed quite rapidly. The latter was nurtured by an oversupply of calories from a bounteous garden.

The realities of the ministry soon mutilated my glowing seminary dreams of a magnanimous pastorate. Even seminary days were tinged with a few unpleasantries which should have been ample proof that life is not always fringed with roses. For one thing, I lacked sufficient funds to support me in the manner in which I wanted to be supported. In fact,

I had less than a hundred dollars to sustain me for nine months. Well, like the fellow who ate a bounteous meal and told the manager he had no money, I was ushered into the kitchen. I, too, had to wash dishes or vamoose.

The proceeds from this menial task were enough to fatten me up a little, put clothes on my back, and a jingle in my pockets. I shaved my face, combed my hair, and cleaned my teeth, then strutted out periodically to call on a lovely blue-eyed damsel.

Courting was a rare experience for me. I'd never had time nor money for females, so, even the anticipation of this unusual event made my heart go pitty-pat. The girl, however, was well schooled in the art of romanticism. She knew when to cuddle up, then withdraw, cuddle more, purr like a kitten, then pull away. I plunged into the sea of matrimony lock, stock, and barrel. To me, wedding bells resounded over hill and dale. The anticipated joys of marital bliss lifted me to a high pinnacle of celestial splendor. That is, until the day my fairy queen told me a young prince had knocked on her door, so my companionship with her could now be graciously terminated.

To say my balloon was deflated is an understatement. I wilted like a flower plucked at noonday, and it took a lot of doing to undo the romantic threads wrapped so tightly around my heart.

Time has a way of unlocking unusual doors, so by the end of another year, my mind had turned a complete revolution and I struggled with the tantalizing problem of pastoral guidance. What groping church needed a good shepherd to lead it in paths of righteousness.

Unfortunately, I missed the train that stopped where the socially elite showered their pastor with gold, and found myself stranded among the gaunt, sun-baked faces of a dust-bowl congregation. Since money was a scarce commodity and the scattered parishioners few, I preached in three different churches.

About the only bright spot in this desert parish was the sun. It came up bright and early, each morning, and set late at night. This made the day long, hot, and lonesome. Lonesome, because I had not yet taken unto myself a helpmate. Oh, there were a few belles of the West but, generally, they were brown, hard, and rangy like the country in which they lived. Anyway, I was busy.

Every other week was spent away from home ministering to the needs of mavericks who had moved to the periphery of my pastoral range. My days were spent wandering over the range looking for strays and my nights were disturbed by rats in some wind-blown bunkhouse. On Sunday, a few straggling souls gathered at the church to sing revival hymns and listen to my words of wisdom. The necktie tenors, bullfrog basses, cracked altos, and screeching sopranos made quite a chorus. What it lacked in quality it made up in volume.

Monday morning, I drove home to clean house. First I'd get a shovel and scoop out the dust that had accumulated during the week. Anyone who has ever lived in the dust bowl can sympathize with my aching back. There was a bright spot, however, for once rid of the first layer, I could proceed with the broom and mop which permitted me to straighten up a little. Although my parsonage had only two rooms, this cleaning process took most of the day.

Before leaving to try my luck in greener pastures, I asked a buxom blonde with soft blue eyes and baby skin to share my future. She was still in her youthful visionary age and grabbed at the chance to escape the ravages of this suffocating dust and blistering sun. Happily, we were also in love.

In our first parsonage I looked at a crack in the dining room floor, glanced at the wall with its designs of large yellow flowers now faded and dimmed by years of accumulated dust, smoke, and grease, and said, "My dear, it looks as if some things need the touch of an artistic hand before this house becomes a home."

Her eyes twinkled, and a coquettish twitch of her lips made the task seem less arduous when she said, "Lover boy, one of the advantages of marrying a desert-trained girl is her adaptation to hard work. Now if you get the necessary accouterments, we'll transform this coliseum into a cosy little home."

This desert queen was mistress of her domicile, whether Romanesque or Church Acquired. There was no mistake about the artistic design of this house —it was Church Acquired. Unfortunately, the living quarters we inherited throughout the years from our predecessors were designed on this same general church poverty-stricken style. One colossal house had four stories. We were like peas rattling around in an overgrown pod.

Well, decades passed and my preaching became a teaching ministry with fourteen little hellions running helter-skelter through the schoolhouse. It took a lasso to slow them down long enough to eat, let alone study.

Getting a school was not like picking apples off a tree. Like a baby learning to walk, my first step was simply teaching. I first took a job as a substitute.

The novice teacher is both lost and scared stiff his first day in school. I arrived ahead of schedule, was assigned a definite room, and in a few minutes thirty-five boys and girls swarmed by me. I'd faced all kinds of congregations for twenty-five years, but this band of hoodlums frightened me. What could I do with their minds? Once more I scanned the lesson plans and there, suddenly, before my eyes was the answer. Let them take a written test and leave the papers for the regular teacher to grade. Poor kids, subjected to an ignorant teacher they had to suffer the consequences. In the course of about fifty minutes, that bunch filed out and another horde streamed in. Somehow, I managed to get rid of six separate groups that day and went home tired, bedraggled, and probably a little wiser.

It took some doing to find a school willing to take a chance on my uninformed knowledge of school procedure and child disciplinary measures. I applied here and there, but every place already had a lot of wonderful applications. Eventually, as so often is the case, one school board was so hard up for a teacher the clerk sent me a contract. I was elated, hallelujah, praise the Lord, now the money would roll in. How was I to know no other teacher would have that school? Well, maybe what you don't know doesn't hurt you. I was as happy as a young mamma with her newborn babe.

Now I would have to get a permit to teach school. Since I was new at this business, the state gave me a year of grace. If I could earn six credits and measure up to numerous other standards, I would qualify for a five-year certificate. The year of grace permitted me to teach while earning the necessary credits for a standard certificate. It eased financial worries, gave me a feeling of importance, elevated my ego, and I faced the world with an optimistic view. Even extra hours of study possessed a glow of accomplishment rather than the pessimistic drag of failure.

If anyone thinks earning six credits is a snap, they better think again. I burned midnight oil reading, studying, and writing. After an eternity, I finished three hours and had only three more to go. Upon the advice of a college professor who had been a Sunday school teacher in my church, I took an easy extension course. After about four months, I passed the course and sent to the state educational department for my certificate. In a few weeks, a large official letter came, which I quickly opened to make sure the worst was over. But low and behold, my mouth fell open and eyeballs bulged like knots on a log. I was flabbergasted. My last three hours did not apply on an elementary certificate, and my school was elementary. Fortunately, I'd lived long enough to learn it doesn't do much good to cry over spilt milk. Once in the stream it's best to keep paddling even though the going gets rough, because your chance of survival increases with your energetic output. With this in mind, I applied for a correspondence course and worked like a beaver another four months to earn another three hours. This time the gods were with me, and my certification was affirmed.

Before meeting my pupils, I had to attend a county teacher's institute. This was an all-day affair where you listened to the county superintendent, a jovial lady as broad as she was long, elaborate on the values of her program. Then a teacher, tried and true, gave the merits of her experience, another presented the rules of the game, then we ate, gathered up a lot of useless material, and went home. I was the only male in the midst of thirty or more women. All of them save one had taught many winters. Out of this heterogeneous assemblage of consecrated females, I was to draw a co-worker. Eagerly, I listened when the names and places of employment were given and, glory be, the young girl was to be my helper. Oh, she wasn't a beauty queen but at least she could walk without a cane and wore a creditable dress instead of a tent. I breathed a sigh of relief.

My schoolhouse outshown the teachers. Although it was small—a-two-teacher, two-room building—it was a new, modern brick building with tile floor and several glass-colored brick windows. Although twenty miles from town, it was on a four-lane highway. My first day in school was a revelation. The double plate glass doors led to a spacious hallway with soft green walls and a lovely tile floor tinted with flecks of gray. I walked up a short stairway, noticed the chrome-plated coatrack in the corridor, and went into my room. I was chief here, not one of the braves. I wore the feathers and gave the orders. In church, every Tom, Dick, and Harry who put a nickle in the collection plate owned the building and employed the preacher. Here there were no offering plates, just a congregation compelled to attend services regardless of weather or sermon. I breathed a sigh of relief. My morning attendance was assured.

Despite an inner dread of what the day might bring, the room was rather cheerful. There were large green-tinted chalkboards on either end. It occurred to me the old blackboard of yesterday had been transformed into a greenboard. I guessed I'd have to change my school vocabulary and keep up with the times. Above the bookshelves, completely covering one side, were transparent windowpanes hidden by Venetian blinds and above them translucent glass bricks which gave the room plenty of light. The opposite wall had a large bulletin board. The desks bothered me. What to do with them was the sixty-four dollar question. How to arrange them? The teacher's desk was in front, which reminded me of a Model T Ford. It had a crank in front and a lot of nuts behind. I pushed my desk to the rear.

It wasn't long before the kids came in. The girls in freshly ironed dresses, and the boys wearing cowboy boots and jeans. Characteristic of a good teacher, I said, "Good morning, boys and girls."

Like well-mannered children, they said, "Good morning, teacher."

Now what was I supposed to say? I couldn't just stand there and gawk at them. They were equally ill at ease. Huddled together like a bunch of sheep, they stood first on one foot, then the other, wringing their hands and twisting their clothes. I finally emerged out of my trance long enough to say, "Boys and girls, it's a few minutes before school time, but since there is a lot of preliminary work, I believe we'll start choosing and adjusting our seats. Perhaps it would be better if the smaller children sat toward the front."

The response was slow and orderly. Mouths were still glued shut, but evidently each pupil had already chosen a seat, because they knew exactly where to go. I got a wrench and adjusted the seats one by one. The only thing anyone said was "Yes," even if their feet dangled from the floor.

Our next item on the agenda was books. I started with three eighth-grade boys and managed to find from one to three books in each subject. One seventh-grade Negro boy was equally fortunate. My sixth-graders learned to their sorrow I could supply them with sufficient subject matter. The cream of the crop was five fifth-grade girls—Mexican twins, a slender Negro, a buxom white girl, and a lovely

Indian maiden. I loved these little girls in spite of their shy and withdrawn attitude. After a fruitless search for material, I said to the girls, "It looks as if we'll just have to get along for a while with what books we have."

Sharon, the pretty little Indian, smiled and suggested, "Maybe we girls can study together."

I asked "Would you study or visit?"

Now the ice was broken, and they all chirped, "Oh, we would study."

"Real hard"? I asked.

"Yes," they cried, "real hard."

I had won the girls. It was love at first sight. Now I would have to charge the impregnable fort that protected the boys. Tear down their barricade and win their confidence.

CHAPTER II

I STUDIED THE BOYS

The boys were normal boys with a desire for knowledge but not an inclination to acquire it through the utilization of mental and physical energy. For example, when I asked my three eighth-grade boys whether they had completed a certain arithmetic assignment, Milton answered, "Yes, I finished it quite awhile ago."

I said, "O.K., that's fine," and turned my attention to the other boys. After some discussion about their impending difficulties, I encouraged them to keep trying until they arrived at a clear understanding of their lesson before going on to new work. A firm foundation certified the construction of a sound mental computer but a flimsy bottom permitted scatterbrain ideas. With this word of wisdom, I dismissed the class and examined the work of several other pupils, then sauntered over to inspect the superior work of Milton. I casually fingered his paper and said, "Let's see the technique you used in working yesterday's problems." He showed me a paper with a lot of figures that didn't make sense,

13

so I pointed to an example he should have known how to work and said, "Here, try this one." He started writing down numbers and was soon lost in a maze of complicated figures without the least idea what to do. I watched him a few minutes, then said, "Milton, I wish you would work this particular series of problems this way." I took his pencil and showed him how to solve them. His relief was obvious, because I had not embarrassed him. Happily, he did all the problems over and gradually learned not to evade difficult tasks or make an attempt to cover up his ignorance of a particular lesson.

John struggled with arithmetic even more than Milton, but either his mind functioned so slowly he never thought of skipping problems or he held a preconceived notion that each example possessed a sacred connotation that required its ultimate solution.

Clarence simply slaved away, never permitting a difficult task to deter him from marching forward. It never occurred to him a lesson was beyond his mental ability to master it. He kept plugging along until the impossible was achieved.

It was Mike and Gordon who kept the wheels of progress turning and sowed seeds of restlessness in our sedate school. They were good boys, but two boys, which means any mischievousness precipitated by one was multiplied by two.

It was natural that these boys should react similarly. Their grandparents were originally from Mexico. The boys each spent a few weeks vacation among their relatives in New Mexico, and understood

14

enough Spanish to hold a limited conversation with older relatives who spoke their mother tongue. Physically, both were small of bone and agile. Their most unique difference lay in their scholastic ability. Gordon was more studious, had a broader comprehensive mind, keener intellect, and retained facts more readily than Mike. He automatically became Mike's intellectual crutch.

Mike was a good boy. His ready wit, agile physique, pleasant disposition, and religious zeal made him a favorite of both boys and girls. Oddly enough, Mike's concept of sin never interfered with the use of unscrupulous methods necessary in meeting school assignments.

Gordon's church covered a broader aspect of life than Mike's. Gordon felt qualms of guilt for any unfair methods in scholastic attainment, but this did not include helping Mike. Spelling, for example, often required their combined thinking to get a satisfactory grade with a minimum amount of effort. Although both boys could, usually, spell all their words, Mike had occasional slip-ups and had to take his lesson over. When this happened, he studied it by writing down all the words with sufficient pressure to leave an imprint on the underneath sheet. A skillful boy with a forgetful teacher could occasionally pull this trick without mishap.

Another aggravating class was poetic memorization and interpretation. A few simple innovations helped minimize the amount of energy required to master assignments in memorization. While Mike recited his poem, Gordon would twist and turn in his chair, opening and closing his book as he fidgeted around. Mike could do the same for Gordon. The only flaw in this maneuver was an unreliable teacher who did the most unexpected things at the most inconvenient times. For example, such as saying, "I think you did a pretty good job reciting, so write the poem today and hand it in. I want every word spelled correctly, every capital letter, comma, period, etcetera."

If Mike knew the poem, all was well, but if he had faked memorization, he'd say, "We need another day to study."

I'd come back with, "It seems to me you recited it quite well."

To which Mike would reply, "It's a lot harder to write. I can't spell all the words or put in all the commas."

"What's the matter?" I'd inquire. "Your recitation indicated a thorough knowledge of the poem."

Gordon's retaliation eased the tension for Mike, "There were a few places where we were uncertain," he'd explain. "Anyway, perfection requires greater study. We could probably have it perfect tomorrow."

"All right," I'd say, "and be sure you know every jot and tittle in the morning."

Both boys usually felt victorious and chimed, "We'll have it O.K. tomorrow."

Gordon usually came through on a second trial, but if for some reason Mike couldn't write a perfect paper, he had two alternatives. One was to ask for a reprieve and extension of time. If this failed, he could lift up the top of his desk and glance at an open book inside. Occasionally, I caught him trying to cheat, but Mike mastered these skills better than the art of retaining subject matter. Obviously the question comes, why did you let pupils get by with such irregular methods of study? My only alibi is that children have always found helps even under the most rigid instructors. I believe the development of a personality has precedence over regimentation. The child who does no wrong because the teacher says, "No, you mustn't," is a puppet to be moved at will. If I caught Mike copying, which I did on rare occasions, I simply had him stay in and rewrite his lesson. To me, fear is a poor criterion for desire. I endeavored to develop a desire for learning in my pupils. This did not necessarily eliminate pranks, and many irregularities in class recitation were considered pranks rather than cheating.

Pranks have been characteristic of boys as long as there have been boys. Although frequently found guilty of a misdemeanor, Mike was not always the instigator of it. Gordon was often the master mind. For example, a neighboring teacher came over to teach my pupils how to use oil paints. The morning went by without a mishap. Unfortunately, however, we never dismissed for recess and took a very short noon. As the hours dragged by, our pupils became increasingly restless. One by one they left their own painting to see how the other fellow was getting along. Naturally, Mike came over to watch Gordon, who was making a portrait of Bart, another sixth-grader.

"Why did you screw his eyes up?" Mike asked Gordon.

"That's the way he looks," Gordon countered. "Anyway, the eyes don't bulge out of their sockets like the one you painted of George."

"My painting looks natural," Mike's whisper increased in volume. "Look at those buck teeth. Bart looks like a papa squirrel scolding mamma. After all, Bart has more than two front teeth."

"I know," murmured Gordon. "A good artist makes certain characteristics more pronounced for emphasis, like you tried to do on George. His chin looks like a bunion on the end of a U-necked squash." At this point Gordon dabbed a blob of paint on Mike's arm. He returned to his picture before a teacher caught him disturbing the peace.

A few minutes later Bart took, liberally interpreted, a coffee break from his modeling job, sauntered over to Mike, grabbed a brush, and smeared green paint on half his face. Mike retaliated by painting Bart from hair to waist. Naturally, the teacher stepped in, but the next morning Bart's mother was in school bright and early for an explanation of how her little darling got so much paint on his clothes. Why didn't the teachers watch their pupils? Bla, bla, bla! This was my first tongue lashing for negligence of duty. Whether I handled the situation wisely is a question for conjecture. I simply told the good sister what we were trying to do and what took place. It was merely a spontaneous reaction of boys who had been confined to a tedious task for several hours. Although

18

this was a long time for boys and girls to work, it served as an excellent experience in self-discipline. Obviously, there was a negative reaction, but no major crime had been committed. Well, after one final lecture the mother left.

Another prank used periodically in our school was putting thumbtacks on one of the seats. One such incident could start a chain reaction that would last until the teacher demanded a halt. Several weeks or even months might pass before it broke out again and became a fad.

In my boyhood days it was a temptation to find your friends in the old swimming hole and tie their clothes in knots or hide them in the brush. This same desire was expressed a little differently in our school. Our classroom was on the first floor and the restrooms in the basement. To reach the basement, a boy had to pass a line of coats hanging neatly on a coatrack. Obviously it was an impossibility for a boy to pass those coats every day and not molest them.

At first, they tied the sleeves of the girls coats together or hid the coats downstairs. I explained that this was a good trick but very impractical, in view of the fact it delayed the girls from getting on their bus on time. Since this prank reached beyond the orbit of teacher-pupil relationship, it should be stopped.

My explanation had a tangible effect, but I soon learned the lower class pupils were finding their coats in various odd places. Their teacher, an antique who had replaced my young teacher, was sure my boys were the villains, so I jumped straddle of their

19

necks and warned them I would not tolerate their molesting the little people.

Gordon, the spokesman on this occasion, said, "We didn't get their coats. A lot of times they throw them down in the hallway or even outside."

"What about yesterday when Sam hid Bobo's coat?" I asked.

"That's the only time," Sam rose to defend himself. "That was at noon, so it didn't interfere with getting on the bus. Anyway," he continued, "their teacher never lets them out until five or ten minutes after the bus comes."

"What their teacher does is her business," I was firm. "But what you do is my business. If you fool with the little kids, you'll have to pay for it."

About a week later the teacher of the small ones barged into my room with a wet coat and said, "Look at this!"

I looked at the boys. Each boy insisted, "I didn't do it."

I looked back at the teacher, who apparently was dissatisfied, for in a biting tone she asked, "What are you going to do about it?"

My reply was very calm but emphatic, "Nothing, you heard the boys."

She whirled and stomped back to her room. I faced the boys once more and in a hard, stern voice asked, "All right, who did it?"

Sam felt branded because he had been guilty on another occasion, so he became the spokesman. "We aren't guilty. Raymond left his coat outside on a hand railing and the wind probably blew it in the snow."

I considered this a good explanation and dropped the subject. The next day, however, a board member appeared in school to settle the coat problem.

My anger flared up at this point, and I informed him I was getting tired of having my boys blamed for things they didn't do. I refused to punish them on the blind accusation of a teacher who was never outside, either at recess or noon, to take care of her pupils. I recognized my kids weren't angels, but at least I tried to keep an eye on them. I'm not sure this little speech did any good but it got a load off my chest.

The board member gave my pupils a free lecture on the value of coats, then left. I'm sure this was unnecessary interference, but what teacher can control a board member? Evidently he didn't know that pranks soon run their gamut of interest. Unfortunately, parents are slow in learning this same fact.

The coat episode would have lost its thrill just as quickly without the aid of a board member. In my room it gave way to coming in late at recess or noon. This was started by the girls. They went for a hike and returned about thirty minutes late. They pleaded innocent of any criminal intent on the grounds none of them owned a watch. The boys and I went into a huddle and decided they should stay in one recess, which was only half the time they were out.

A few days later I was helping the boys clean out an old building to be used for recreational purposes.

When we returned, the girls were hard at work and yelled in unison, "You're fourteen minutes late. You'll have to stay in fourteen minutes because we took up school on time."

The boys came back with, "No we don't, because our teacher was with us."

"That doesn't make any difference," countered the girls. "It only adds to your guilt because he has a watch."

I felt obligated to defend the boys and argued, "In my humble opinion the boys are justified in their contention, not because I was with them but because we were actually doing schoolwork. The lack of text-books should not minimize the importance of the job."

The Negro girl insisted we all stay in. "The work you did," she said, "may be a benefit to the boys but not the girls. Since its purpose was to help only one part of the student body, it can't be called school-work."

Obviously we weren't getting any place, so I suggested we bring the matter before the school court at a future date. The boys objected on the grounds our chief justice was a girl. I insisted the court of law was the proper place to settle our differences, so the matter was dropped and we settled down to schoolwork. Whether the boys were right in their contention that we could never get a fair trial still remains an unanswered question. Be that as it may, the trial was held, with Gordon as our lawyer. I gave him considerable assistance and thought we presented a pretty good case. In fact, I expected an acquittal, but we lost our case and had to stay in fourteen minutes. Actually, the boys didn't seem to mind. They held a great deal of respect for our chief justice and fully appreciated the pressure under which she pronounced sentence. After all, this was school and they all let off vocal steam at the trial. This was good mental gymnastics, but every case did not go to court. In fact, some problems were never made public.

One day Sharon said to me, "I bring candy to school for a recess snack, but the last few days someone has taken it our of my dinner pail."

"You shouldn't eat candy anyway," I chuckled. "It will add pounds to your good looks."

She smiled in her own sweet way and said, "Thanks for the compliment." Then she continued in a soft feminine tone rather than the chirp of a twelve-year-old, "I don't eat enough candy to make me fat."

My next question was designed to probe for a clue that might rout out the thief. "Does your brother have candy in his dinner pail?"

"Of course." She seemed puzzled. "I usually fix both lunches the same way."

"Does anyone take his candy?" was my next question.

"No, I'm sure they don't or he would have mentioned it. What does that have to do with me?" she wanted to know.

"It may not have anything to do with you." I was voicing my thoughts more than speaking to her. "It just happens when I was a boy of thirteen, very much attracted to a girl who looked very much like you, I remember I did a lot of foolish things to get her attention." I looked straight into Sharon's eyes, "How many boys like you?"

My question never revealed the least indication of surprise. Obviously her thoughts were in perfect harmony with mine, for she answered quickly and frankly, "Two, Ted and Sam."

"They both use innumerable ways to attract your attention, do they not?"

"Yes." She spoke quite slowly, "It's a little difficult to explain because I can't tell you what they do. Sometimes its a look, a paper wad, they walk past my desk to sharpen a pencil, flick water in my face, I don't know, a lot of personal things."

"They may not be the culprits?" I spoke with a question mark. "My guess is, however, that if you put your lunch pail near your desk or in an empty bookcase, the thief will disappear." Then I added, "I think it's unwise to let this practice continue, even though your food is taken by a Romeo."

She smiled sweetly and said, "I'll try your suggestion," and went out to play.

A couple of weeks later I asked how the plan worked and she said, "It worked fine. I'm putting my lunch pail back with the others now."

"We all live and learn," I agreed, "whether young or old." Then I added, "Especially when dealing with women." She gave me a knowing look and left. This twelve-year-old girl was playing her men with the skill of an adult.

In our school the usual things happened that have been automatic digressions of school discipline for decades, such as periodic excursions to the restrooms, which can be controlled to a degree, but like one little sixth-grade said, "when you gotta go you gotta go." What teacher can tell for sure whether the boy or girl had home or school disturbances that affected him or her physically?

An unquenchable thirst can be redirected if rigid restrictions are imposed. The boy who breaks the lead on his pencil becomes more careful if his unfinished task is completed at recess. One almost uncontrollable crime is running down the hallway or down stairs. Even perfect pupils are tempted to run after a friend in the corridor. Our system worked fairly well because each pupil helped to enforce it. If a pupil was caught running, he had to go back and walk. This was both embarrassing to the speedster and required valuable time that could have been utilized in play.

If something was thrown in the classroom, such as a ball, an eraser, a pencil, a book, or any other article, the culprit stayed in to write one hundred times, "I will not throw erasers," or whatever was thrown, "in the schoolhouse." The effectiveness of this system depends largely upon the co-operation of the pupils.

Chewing gum received the same punishment. My boys and girls contended that unless I, personally, caught them chewing gum, eating candy, etc., they were not subject to punishment. This gave them a little leeway because if one student told me to watch a particular person, a close friend inevitably warned the guilty one, which made detection very difficult. It was a good game, however, and I think enjoyed by everyone. I'm sure the rule against gum chewing could have been enforced more effectively at the loss of its glamour and challenge.

Pranks are only one phase of school life. The good school patrons wanted to see their offspring perform, particularly at Christmas. We were like all other schools and did our best to comply with parental pressures. We chose a couple of plays that seemed fairly well adapted to our school. One play was more desirable than the other so, naturally, each boy and girl wanted the leading part in it. I assigned the parts with considerable care, then wrote down the characters on the chalkboard. Starting with the most important, I wrote a student's name opposite each character. As I wrote, I explained why I chose a particular boy or girl. When I finished, Gordon and Sharon held the major parts. I wasn't sure how the others would react because Gordon was in the sixth grade and Sharon in the fifth so, turning to the school, I asked, "Are there any comments or objections?" Milton, Sharon's older brother, said, "I think you've done a good job." I was relieved because Milton was by and large the school's spokesman.

Pressing the matter a little further, however, with an effort to add a bit of humor, I asked, "How about you, Mike, you don't have a love scene."

Judy popped up, "He can't learn what he has so don't give him any more."

"O.K. for you blabbermouth," Mike countered. "I'll know my part before you do yours."

Ruth sprang to her feet. "Judy and Mike probably want a love scene together. He's always over at her house."

Julie flew to the defense of her twin. "He comes over to play with Gordon, not Judy. Anyway," she paused a moment, "that has nothing to do with our cast. I think it is all right. I'm willing to learn my part and do the best I can."

"Let's take a vote," I suggested. "Everybody in favor of producing the play as presented here signify by raising your right hand." Hands were raised from every seat, nevertheless I added, "All opposed the same sign." There were no negative votes. "The motion is carried." I announced, "Now, let's get to work on our lessons. You can study your parts to-night." Out came their readers and five girls gathered around my desk ready to read their lesson.

The play moved forward in a fine way. Sharon and Gordon proved as adept to characterization and willing to work as I anticipated. They studied expression, took voice exercises, and soon became seasoned performers. I thought everything was fine and the play would go over better than most plays produced by elementary pupils. Actually we were ready, but on the evening of the program Sharon was standing near the coatrack with a look of dejection on her face. "What's the matter, Sharon?" I asked.

The lines on her face were drawn and she looked even more ghastly through the grease paint. She looked at me through tear-stained eyes and said, "I feel sick and have a headache."

I put my arm around her, patted her hair, and said, "Don't worry, young lady. It's probably stage fright. Once you get on the stage, you'll forget everything except the play." Quickly her sickness vanished, because her greatest need was encouragement and attention. After we walked a few steps, I asked, "Do you feel better?"

"Yes, I'm all right now. I guess you're right, I'm just frightened."

True to my prediction, her fright left and I knew for sure her headache was forgotten because in a few minutes she and Gordon were playing their parts like professionals.

The next year we chose Dickens' "Christmas Carol," and I asked the students to name the characters. I guess they respected my judgment, because Gordon and Sharon were again given leading parts and worked with the same fervor they did the first year.

In our third year we decided to write a play. This year Vivian played opposite Gordon, and Sharon took charge of the music. She was older now and had an exceptionally good voice. In order to put her in the proper perspective she took the part of a Western cowhand. Decked in a ten-gallon hat, bandana, jeans, and boots, she certainly looked like a movie star. She didn't need a horse and six-gun to become an intricate part of the play.

Gordon worked with the same tenacity as other years but forgot his role in a scene where his daughter, who was his sister in real life, was very sick and had to be carried into another room. Gordon did fine in rehearsal but on the night of the play he had some trouble in picking her up and, before he reached the stage door, dropped her on the floor. Fortunately, the sick girl landed on her feet and quickly made an exit, but the audience saw how quickly the critically ill little girl became well and a serious scene took on a humorous note that made it difficult to recover the spirit of the play. Barring this one incident, the play measured up to our highest expectations.

In one play, a seventh-grade boy had to hold hands with Vivian. At first they looked at each other and repeated their parts. I let this go for a few rehearsals, then insisted they hold hands with the warmth designated by the script. Their first attempt was a hurried touch, so I made them try again. This time they took hold of hands but each looked the other way. After six or seven more trials, they finally looked at each other with a small degree of warmth. The next rehearsal was a repetition of our first real attempt at intimacy. This was an age of romanticism at a distance, not close proximity before an audience, particularly with schoolmates.

Play practice had its diversions. In order to maintain a semblance of quiet, I put Sam by my feet,

Dale along one wall, Ted on the stage, Dick in the middle of the auditorium, Ralph where I could watch him and the girls in front of the stage. Inevitably, when I allowed more than one actor behind the curtain, there was a clang and clatter of fallen props. Sometimes a giggle, a loud whisper, a whistle, or just milling around caused distraction. Quietness for over two minutes was an impossibility with ten-to twelve-year-olds. Even thirteen-year-old boys are still juvenile and girls are in the giggly stage. I've tested them for quietness several times and out of fourteen pupils someone always snickered within one minute.

True, they weren't always bad. When on the stage, each character tried to play his part. Gordon made an effort to control himself and younger boys gathered around him. Sharon was always the well-poised young lady, Vivian a well-mannered student, and the others were usually as good or better than the average student, so I had little complaint.

I had a great admiration for Gordon. He was alone in the eighth grade and an idol of all the boys. He had always been a good sport and handled himself with some agility. As a sixth-grader he took some hard knocks in football from three large eighth-grade boys, then, when spring arrived they ordered him to play certain positions in softball, which he accepted without complaint. This co-operative spirit enabled the boys to have a winning softball team. The next year Gordon was the only boy bold enough to tackle a larger eighth-grader who could plow through the entire team. Then came Gordon's last year in school.

Now he was chief. Like his predecessors, he practically made up one team in football. I noticed this about Gordon, however, although he ran hard and played hard, he was careful not to hurt his opponents. This not only made for good sportsmanship but added to the enthusiasm of the game. Each morning one of the smaller boys would say, "I get to play with Gordon today," so they hurried outside to line up, two boys against four. I usually played center for both teams and acted as referee.

Spring was a little more exciting because all the boys would eventually play softball against a neighboring school. This school refused to play them the year Gordon was in the seventh grade because of a beating they had taken when our school had three eighth-grade boys. This year, however, they were confident they could beat us, so plans were made for a big contest. I listened to my boys boast how they would trample the other team in the dust. In fact, I thought they were a bit too cocky and had a tendency to let up on their practice. One day I said to Gordon, "I doubt very much that you can beat Redrock unless our young fifth-grade boys learn to handle that ball."

Gordon had already caught some of their conceit and declared in fervent tones, "Oh, we'll beat them easy, don't worry."

I insisted the other team had better boys this year. "You know the Redrock boys," I said. "They have three pretty good fellows, and you're the only boy we have able to hit or catch the ball." I reminded him of a practice game they held just a week before in which Redrock was ahead when I called them in for their district achievement test.

Gordon was in no mood to accept defeat and reaffirmed his victorious position, "Oh, we'll win all right. Both Ted and Dick can bat the ball and Ted is getting so he can catch it so I'm sure we'll be ready for them."

"If you're so positive," I decided to test Gordon's assertion, "I'll tell you what I'll do. If you win against Redrock, I'l buy each of you a Coke, but if you lose you buy me a Coke."

The boys were not satisfied to let Gordon in on this deal alone so they yelled, "We'll do it. If we lose, each of us will buy you a Coke."

"O.K.," I was firm, "it's a deal because I'm sure you'll lose and I'll need six Cokes to bolster my morale."

"You mean we'll each have a Coke to celebrate our victory?" they shouted. "We'll trample all over that bunch."

"You'll have to get a lot better than you are now if you want to win. Just look at this motley bunch of awkward cows. Gordon is the only one who can hit or catch the ball, and they have three hitters. Ted hits about one out of four and the rest of you bat like women."

Gordon came to their rescue, "Dick can hit a hard ball when he hits, Dale is getting better, and Ralph does fairly well at shortstop."

"O.K," I said, "I'll tell you what I'm going to do.

I'm going to watch you a few more days, then assign your positions. Once they are assigned, I want you to play them until the game. There will be no changing off. Each fellow will play his position regardless of how sloppy he plays it. It'll be up to him to learn the position and not let the team down." I paused to let this sink in, then added, "Now that we know the score, let's forget ball and take up school to try your skill with books." Their response to books was a lot of groans and moans, but the fatal hour had arrived from which there was no reprieve.

A few days later I heard Gordon barking to his teammates, "Catch that ball, you clumsy ox, pick up that grounder and act like a man. This isn't a girl's game." A fly was missed. Dale held up his gloved hand and stood back for fear he might catch the ball. Gordon yelled, "Two hands, you dumb cluck, don't be such a coward." I saw Gordon burn one to Ted, who stepped aside and let it pass, "Get in there, you sissy, and catch the ball. What do you want to do, play with the girls?"

"You threw it too hard," Ted yelled back "It hurts my hand."

"Well, use your glove," Gordon roared. "What do you have it on for?"

At this point I stepped in the fray and called a huddle. "Listen, you babies," I said, "when you catch a ball let your hand move back with it and you can catch most any ball. Take two hands. Try to get the ball in the pocket of your glove and move with it. Now get out there and get hurt instead of playing like babies."

The boys were soon playing with the courage of little leaguers, but it wasn't easy to always maintain a winning spirit, for try as they would the ball never seemed to be in the right place. Both Gordon and I kept whipping them into shape. I kidded them about the six Cokes, which seemed to serve as a stimulant for better practice.

When the day arrived for our game, the boys were ready. They might lose, but each fellow knew where he was to play and, whether good or bad, he would do his best.

The Redrock team arrived confident of victory. Their teacher was the referee. A couple of times my boys complained about unfair decisions, but I told them to play the game and accept the penalties. "We will win above reproach or we'll not win at all," I insisted.

The boys took the lead and held it. In the first inning Gordon came to bat with the bases loaded and hit a homer. He did the same thing in the second inning, so their spirits remained high throughout the game. When it was over, the boys came to me with their complaints. "The other team cheated," they contended. "In practice, you let us run when the catcher missed the ball but you made us stay on base today. We could have made a bigger score."

"Now hold your horses." I held up my hands for silence. "I know you're right but you won the game. The Redrock catcher couldn't catch the ball, which would have made the score very uneven. As it is, you're happy because you won, they feel like it was a good game, so they'll probably play again next year. Everybody is happy. Isn't that better?"

"Yeah, it's O.K. by us," they shouted in chorus. Then came the thunderous roar, "Say, we won the game, when do we get our Cokes?"

"Don't worry," I tried to shout above the turmoil, "you really won fair and square so I'll bring the Cokes tomorrow."

"Hurrah! Hurrah!" they shouted and ran away. Actually, the game was forgotten and the Cokes unimportant. Their greatest victory was not over Redrock but over their teacher.

Gordon still had a number of things to do before the day was over. He was graduating this year and had a speech to rehearse, as this district expected each graduate to give a résumé of his school experience. The speech and other things pertaining to graduation had been a mental strain on Gordon, who had worked hard all year, but now it was about over and his relief was tremendous.

One extra burden during the year was my insistence that he learn a band instrument. As a school, we studied music through the use of tonettes. About Christmas time, during my second year as a teacher, my older girls decided I left something to be desired as a music instructor, so they exchanged tonettes for piano and voice. I knew less about either of these, but they were different and the girls went to them like a duck goes to water. Gordon was out on a limb, because he too had passed the tonette stage. I toyed with the idea of advanced music for him and discussed the feasibility of flute lessons. My daughter never touched her flute any more, so if he wanted to take flute lessons I'd check with her and see whether she would give him lessons. He was quite enthusiastic, so arrangements were made for him to come over each Saturday. She could teach music as it ought to be taught, not in my lumbering haphazard way.

The idea apparently was a good one, for by the end of that school year, Gordon was ready to join a city school band. By fall he had exchanged the flute for a saxophone and was doing so well his parents bought him a new instrument. Naturally, the private lessons stopped, but I helped him pound out his time and bawled him out when he screwed up his notes. He appeared in public a few times and had a couple of numbers ready for his commencement exercise. I was proud of this boy. He was a fine fellow, completely ready for the next step in his scholastic career.

Chapter III

TED COMES TO SCHOOL

Ted's matriculation in our school was a sad day for me. His mother came with him and said, "I have two boys. I understand Ted will be in your room. He has been a problem in other places, so sit right down on him, make him behave, and see that he studies."

I tried to be courteous. "I'm sure he'll be fine," I assured her. "He looks like a good boy to me."

I hoped that would be sufficient but she kept right on. "Ted's brother is a good boy and makes good grades, but Ted doesn't apply himself. You have a good reputation as a teacher, so maybe you can do something with him."

"I assure you I'll do my best," I told her.

After another five minutes of praise and condemnation she left, leaving her juvenile delinquents behind. My job was very simple. All I had to do was transform a sixth-grade imp into an angel with saintly behavior and omniscience.

I was at a disadvantage, because Ted had a stacked deck. His mother was now living with her fourth husband and this screwball left much to be desired.

Ted had completed the fifth grade under strict disciplinary measures, then decided that the beaver, moose, and bear made better instructors than a self-taught spinster who lauded the merits of book learning.

Ted could shoot a thirty-ought-six, follow the trail of an elk, elucidate on the habits of deer, or tell where the groundhog raised her young. To him, however, teachers were a peculiar breed of indecipherable creatures whose concept of realistic values ran amuck in the mire of intellectual confusion. He had tried to unravel stories about Pecos Bill, who grabbed a cyclone by the tail, or Paul Bunyan and his blue ox, a stupendous bull. Little Miss Muffet could sit on a tuffet and eat her curds and whey for all he cared. As for social studies, he never expected to travel beyond the Rockies, so why get all stewed up over other countries? He already knew where the elk lived, which was far more satisfying than the study of topographical maps designed to guess the probable location of his habitat. You didn't need spelling to set a trapline, art to appreciate the mountains, or even arithmetic to keep tab on a fur cache. Schools had little intrinsic value, and teachers were a source of mental anguish. A few pupils had a semblance of good sense, but, generally, they were a polyglot of heterogeneous stooges. Our little school was a melting pot of races. It was like a cosmopolitan city, with whites, Negroes, Mexicans, and Indians. How could a stranger break through the cliques already formed by two-faced kids?

Ted had been in school scarcely a month before he was accused of violating a regulation held sacred by the student body. As a result, he was tried before a student court and found guilty. His sentence was to remove one shoe and kiss his big toe. He rebelled against such an outlandish tactic. Sam decided to act as marshal and force the issue. Ted set him down so hard I came to his rescue, and Ted immediately succumbed to the inevitable. Although teachers were an enigma he could not tolerate, their law was infallible.

I thought the matter was closed. School was dismissed, and everyone filed out to the bus. I went downstairs for a dust mop, took it from the custodian's room, and turned around to go upstairs when a loud, angry voice yelled, "What the hell is going on here?"

I looked up to see a burly giant in front of me. His rough, dirty clothes, heavy black beard, beady eyes, and worn cowboy hat made him look more like a beast than a man. I was scared stiff but asked in a calm, unruffled voice, "Why, what seems to be the matter?"

"Your damned teaching is the matter. My boy came out to the car crying like a baby because of your silly ideas. If it ever happens again, I'll knock your block off."

I didn't cringe, but felt like crawling in a hole. "I'm sorry, I didn't realize we did anything wrong. We have simply organized a school court which should be a help in both instructive and disciplinary measures."

"I don't give a damn what you've done," he barked. "I don't want my boy coming home or out to the car bawling." He started to leave.

Once more I tried to reason with the man. "If you would visit with me and let me explain what we are trying to do, I'm sure things would look different."

He obviously was afraid to face me in verbal combat, so he continued upstairs with this last remark, "You have a reputation of being a good teacher, so I'll leave this time but I warn you if this ever happens again I'll beat you up."

He rushed out of the door and was gone. I went into my room to straighten up books, papers, and desks, clean chalkboards, and dust. The question of what to do under threats and bombastic verbal battering was still unanswered. As a boy, one of my teachers fumbled a similar problem worse than my fifth-grade boys trying to catch a fly.

Her thorn in the flesh was a woman who derived sadistic pleasure in verbal abuse of schoolteachers. Miss Thornburg, my teacher, told her off at periodic intervals and finally succeeded in forcing her to put her sons in another school. I didn't want this. I wanted to prove my ability to handle both the boys and their parents.

Ted's mother was not sure where to stand. My reputation as a teacher made opposition to our school program a slam on her family, and Ted's mother did not want to think of herself in this light. Furthermore, in spite of this little incident, Ted was already forming an attraction for me.

One fly in the ointment was Bart. Bart came from a broken home and, like Ted, returned home each evening to drinking, cursing, frustration, and confusion. Under such repugnant conditions, it was impossible to do homework. Dog eat dog was the household motto. Bart found himself bashed by his stepfather, then alternately cuddled and cursed by his mother, who sought solace for her own wounds rather than love for her son. Bart rebelled against his stepfather's disciplinary measures and mother's hypocrisy. They created an ambivalance which sought release in school frivolity. He sought friends to elevate his ego, who became his victims. Since both Ted and Bart were outsiders, they became fellow conspirators. Both came from broken homes, and both endured home frustrations, quarrels, and community scorn. One major difference lay in their mothers. Ted's mother loved him with a deep sacrificial love, whereas Bart gave of his affection to satisfy the deep craving of a love-starved mother. This left Bart empty, and he tried to fill his spiritual vacuum with frivolous external contacts. When bolstered by love, a boy can stand a lot of battering, but loneliness crushes the noblest soul. Bart needed personal elation even though it was obtained through physical torture. He was not masochistic in seeking flagellation but accepted it as part payment in achieving his sadistic goal. Bart derived a great deal

of pleasure in watching two small boys fight, a larger
boy get spanked, a girl stay in for a misdemeanor he
had masterminded, or a group of pupils get punished
for an infraction of school regulations. Many times I
scolded him, threatened him, or shook him in hopes
of redirecting his energies. He would succumb to
coercive disciplinary measures for short periods of
time but an urgency soon sent him scurrying to a
little boy with faked friendship, in an effort to get
him, or a girl, in trouble.

One evening, while waiting for the bus, he caused
such a disturbance I grabbed him by the shoulders
and squeezed them hard. It must have hurt because
he winced and settled down. The next morning I
had callers. School had already convened, so I wasn't
aware of anyone's arrival until one of the girls told
me I had company.

I went to the door of my classroom and saw Bart's
mother and Ted's parents waiting at the far end of
the corridor. I was frightened, but they had to be
faced, so I walked over and greeted them with a
pleasant, "Good morning."

Ted's mother said, "We came over to talk to you
about our children. You said if we didn't understand
why certain things were done you'd be happy to
explain them to us."

Ted's father grunted, "I told you I'd beat you up
if I ever had to come again."

I answered, "Yes, I know you did," Then I turned
to Ted's mother, "I'll certainly do my best to answer

your questions because we try to conduct a good school."

Bart's mother couldn't keep quiet any longer and growled, "How does it happen our kids are always the ones in trouble? Is it because my name isn't Nelson?" The Nelsons owned several hundred acres of land and raised prize beef cattle.

"No," I assured her. "The Nelson boy was punished just the other day."

"I'll bet you didn't choke him to death like you did my boy," she roared. "If my boy needs to be punished, paddle him on the butt. That's what the good Lord made butts for."

I stammered this time, "If that's what you want, I'll try to oblige. I punished him yesterday in the manner that seemed most effective at the moment."

"You're damn tootin' I want his butt paddled," she screamed. "That's what teachers did when I went to school. If it was good enough then, it's good enough now." Then she added her ace. "If you don't, I'll have my husband come and beat you to a pulp."

I guess the frequent beatings I was promised made my answer trite, "I always try to please parents insofar as it is feasible."

Ted's father felt bold enough to try verbal combat. "I understand you favor the girls over the boys." His voice had tempered a little, as if he wanted a civil answer.

My reply was to the point, "I don't favor the girls but I try to recognize their position as girls. I'm

43

of the old school that believes women have certain special rights. For example, the boys wait for the girls to leave the classroom first." This statement hit home. Even these rough mountaineers placed women on a pedestal. Both of Ted's parents approved of this practice. I had broken the ice, so we were apparently ready to discuss school.

Bart and Ted were called for questioning. Bart admitted stirring up trouble. Ted evaded the issue, but broke under the pressure applied by his mother and admitted his part in several transgressions of school policy. Mike was called from the classroom and tears flooded his eyes under the battering of these self-appointed FBI agents. I'm sure Ted's mother felt she overstepped her bounds. It was not the teacher but an intruder trying to discipline another mother's son. Maybe the teacher had his imperfections, but at least he was hired to guide their children. Obviously Ted's mother felt she was pressing her rights as a school patron, for with an unexpressed feeling of guilt, she immediately took her cohorts from the school.

This was my last session on "How You Should Teach My Boys." Evidently my would-be instructors were convinced any possibility of reforming me was hopeless.

Fortunately, neither Ted nor Bart were any worse for wear as a result of this visit. Perhaps they thought their teacher won the debate and school would proceed according to schedule.

Bart threw a few more tantrums before the end

of that school year. He was never convinced that school could function properly without his personal touch to stimulate adverse behavior and keep the wheels of discontent rolling.

Ted decided his teacher's honesty deserved some merit. To him, the climax had come. He stood at the crossroads of life. One highway led to Bart and his concept of success. The other was traveled by his teacher and those who believed in the supremacy of honesty and service. No rash decision was made; gradually, however, he threw in his lot with his teacher.

Bart could not survive as a lone wolf. He needed cohorts, stooges, renegades, or choreboys to do his work and sing his praises. Sam, although a Nelson, had no close friends. He, too, was hungry for attention. Bart could create the spectacular and win acclaim. True, there were repercussions, but they were negligible in comparison to the daring and courage required in the completion of his feats. Sam chose the downhill road of discontent. He frequently found himself standing alone against the school. His hero often found ways of shifting to neutral ground or even joining his teacher, leaving Sam out on a limb. Some boys learn quickly, but poor Sam was swayed by the silvery words of Bart and accepted his lot rather than lose the glory and grandeur of his idol.

Unlike Bart and Sam, Ted learned there were girls in school. His first public confession of this fact came by accident. We were having a school party and ran short of games, so I suggested an old party game. It was a mystery game in which a queen sat upon her throne and accepted courtiers in her court provided they passed a rigid test. The queen's assistant brought to the throne room a subject who was told about the honor received by anyone invited to join the court. The child was then brought before the queen and asked to kneel on a royal rug at her feet. She explained her desire to have a noble court and had devised a simple test to help discover those worthy to be part of this select group. She then said, "I want you to say, 'Who You Love Best.'" The words "Who You Love Best" were to be repeated.

On this occasion Sharon was dressed as a queen, and I served as her accomplice, or royal guard, to escort the select subjects, who were in another room, one by one to the throne.

The game progressed very nicely. Each pupil brought before Sharon thought the statement was a question to be answered rather than repeated. He or she would say mother, father, sister, brother, cousin, etc. Each time Sharon insisted the subject had not complied with her request. Eventually, however, they all caught the joke and Ted was ushered into this solemn, august group of dignified courtiers. There was no laughter or bantering. This was a serious occasion and every student looked like a judge. Sharon went through her ritual, and Ted sweated under the pressure. Like others, he named relatives or people whose names would not embarrass him. Finally, in desperation, he said, "You."

Sharon never batted an eye and replied, "No, that isn't correct. Just do what I asked. Say, 'Who you love best.' "

Ted was emphatic this time, "I told you the truth. I love you best."

There was a snicker in the room and the entire school closed in on poor Ted, shouting, "Just do what she said, Ted, repeat the words, 'Who you love best.' " Ted was really embarrassed now. He had already made a public confession of his love for Sharon.

From this time on until the close of school there was little object in trying to hide his love. It became an accepted fact. Familiarity made Ted increasingly bold. He sought occasions to be with Sharon and on Valentine's Day they exchanged gifts as well as cards. Sharon, occasionally, encouraged Ted, yet she usually maintained such a marked reserve it was difficult to tell whether she placed his affections above that of the other boys.

The advantage of this courtship from my vantage point was Ted's interest in school. Rather than being driven behind prison walls, he glowed with the bloom of expectation and each morning entered a garden of paradise. The drab pallor of books took on a new radiance when Sharon arrived at school. Even classes held a luster not prevalent before she became the apple of his eye. He was the only boy in the sixth grade with five girls, but this didn't matter if Sharon happened to sit near him. Unfortunately, she had already learned the strategy of a woman and led him on one day, only to crush him beneath the deepest despondency on the next. Neverthless, he continued to fight for her affections with the same tactics evident in adults. His comb became a magnet through usage, there was a bounce in his walk, I thought his tongue was loose at both ends but this merely called Sharon's attention to his reality. Most of all, however, was an obvious interest in scholastic advancement. Sharon was good medicine for Ted. Even his social adjustment and behavior showed a growing transformation.

By the close of school, Ted showed many evidences of improvement. His mother came one morning and asked whether I would be back that fall. I said, "Yes, the board sent me a contract and I signed it. I had thought of going to a larger district, but there were several unfinished jobs in this school that offered me a tremendous challenge."

"I'm certainly glad," she said with a sigh of relief that displayed a concern far greater than was evident in most mothers. "Ted likes you and has made greater strides this year than in all his other years combined."

"It's nice of you to say that," I tried to be casual, "although I've been quite pleased with his mental, spiritual, and social growth." I switched the conversation to her life. "What about Ted's home environment. Is it any better or does he still come home to cursing, drinking, and bickering?"

Her attempted smile was forced, "Conditions aren't any better. Drinking isn't as much a problem as anger. Guy gets mad at both me and the boys. I try to protect them when he gets rough, but as you know, I can't handle him."

"What about food?" I wanted to know. "The boys don't look hungry."

"We have plenty to eat." She brightened up a little.

"He usually gives me an allowance for food. The only difficulty is I hate to give an exact account of everything I buy."

"I can see this would be a little annoying, but perhaps endurable if other conditions were favorable." I paused a moment, "Obviously, one of my concerns is education. Does he encourage the boys in their schoolwork?"

She breathed a sigh of despair, "You know how he is. He only completed the fifth grade and knows more about wild life than most people, so why waste time in school? When he takes the boys out in the woods, they have a good time and he teaches them about nature. Then they idolize him and school suffers."

"What about their real father?" I asked. "Does he give them any encouragement?"

She seemed to choose her words, "Yes, he wants them to plan for college, but it's pretty hard because he has a family of his own." Tears flooded her eyes. "The job is pretty much mine. That's why I'm so grateful for what you've done and so happy you'll be here next year."

I placed my hand on her shoulder, "We have

another nine months, at least, so between us maybe we can sow some good seed that will bear fruit."

She tried to hold back her tears but they dropped on my shoulder. It had been so long since someone offered to share her burdens. I admired this woman, who wanted a good man so very much yet dared to fight alone. Today her problems were still the same, but she left my school with a song in her heart.

When Ted returned to school that fall, he had grown in stature. He didn't seem to mind being a boy in a class with five girls. His first tumble for Sharon had leveled off, and I was not sure she stood any higher in his estimation than the other girls. If anything, he was girl-shy.

I pressed him hard to measure up to the girls. For one thing, his reading was atrocious. I insisted he learn to read as smoothly and fluently as the girls. I did not intend having a bunch of females showing up the males in this school. His answer was always the same, "I can't."

To overcome this negative attitude, I gave him twice as much to read as the girls, with a stipulation that if he didn't do a good job he would have to read at recess. Ted liked his play period, so in the course of months he overcame his inferiority in reading and even asked for larger assignments.

Spelling in the school needed to be improved. On occasions we played baseball in spelling. I would pronounce a word to the batter. He spelled it and took a base. The next batter did the same until a runner scored one point. Three outs or misses and the other team came to bat. Ted invariably fanned out. It was embarrassing, so he hated to play the game. To overcome this deficiency, we inaugurated a plan similar to that used in reading. Slowly, yet steadily, Ted mastered his words until a hundred in spelling was the rule rather than the exception.

The same general procedure was adapted to every class. It meant work, but it brought rewards. Ted gained confidence in himself and forgot his trite excuse of "I can't."

The miracle of Ted's growth came in spite of home frustrations. His mother came to me soon after Christmas. She still walked straight, with a glint of determination in her lovely blue eyes, but new wrinkles were burrowing their way on her round youthful face. The bloom of her checks was being replaced by the pallor of age. She stood by my desk and her lips quivered. "I'm at the end of my rope," her voice was weak, "my whole body is black and blue where Guy beat me."

I tried to show interest without disturbance. "Sit down and tell me about it." I spoke encouragingly for she needed a calm strength.

"He wanted to take the boys to the mountains to learn his latest art in catching mink. I refused to let them go." Her shoulders shook, then straightened. Her jaw became firm as she looked directly into my eyes for assurance. "My boys are not going to grow up as mountain men. This is a civilized age. We are not savages."

"Is that when he beat you?" I asked.

"Yes, the moment I degraded hunting he flew into a rage and hit me with his fist. Ted came to my rescue, but was knocked across the room with one blow. Both boys cowered in the corner. Finally I went down, then Guy kicked me and left."

"What will happen when he returns?" I tried to be understanding.

"Oh, he'll burrow in the mountains like a beast a couple nights until his anger wears off, then he'll come back purring like a kitten." She paused a moment, looked straight at me, and again spoke in a determined voice, "This can't go on. Even if I could take it, I don't want the boys subjected to that type of environment. They'll grow up to be woman beaters."

I knew she had already decided what to do, but needed my sanction so I asked, "What do you intend to do now?"

Her eyes searched mine for sympathetic understanding, "This is the second time we tried to make a go as husband and wife. Why I married him, I don't know. Maybe it's because he can be gentle as a lamb and is all man. You know I've had three other husbands. In other words, I've made a mess of my life." She paused as if fearful to venture on.

I repeated her thoughts, "Now you want a divorce. The muchly married woman did it again."

"Yes." She grabbed my hands as they lay folded on my desk. I placed one hand over hers and leaned toward her, "What will it do to the boys?" She continued, "Naturally, there will be gossip, lots of it."

I stood up and touched her bruised cheek, "It seems to me the key question is what will it do to the boys if you continue to live with him?"

She fell on my neck and sobbed, "I'll have to take the boys out of school, at least one day for the trial."

I let her nerves relax, then stepped behind my desk again to become a teacher. I merely answered, "Yes, I know."

She dabbed her eyes with her handkerchief, said, "Thanks," smiled through her tear-stained face, and left.

Little was said in school about the divorce. Ted had already won his place as a regular pupil.

His ex-stepfather came to school one day to meet his mother and try a reconciliation. The result was a quarrel which intrigued the other students but did not affect their relationship to the boys. Ted's mother left him and went to the home of a neighbor, where she stayed until the officers came to arrest Guy.

Once more she came to me and wondered what to do. Her lawyer had suggested Guy be sent to a mental hospital. Since I had some experience with mental patients, I acquiesced in the lawyer's decision and urged her to file a complaint. It was evident to me that her ex-husband was dangerous and might have to remain under professional care for an indefinite period of time; even if cured, his philosophy of life was so different from her own that a happy family life was impossible.

As for Ted and Dale, they were happy it was all over. Since Guy was not their real father, they regarded him as another unpleasant page in their book of life. School had taken on a new stature for both of them, particularly Ted, whose ideals and behavior were proving the value of patience, encouragement, and understanding. He was no longer a delinquent boy shunned by every teacher, but a scholar marching toward the fulfillment of his destiny.

CHAPTER VI

STUDENT GOVERNMENT

I was accustomed to student councils in college. They seemed to be the normal procedure to camouflage an autocratic dictatorship into a figurehead democracy. Students settled all the small problems, which made their authority negligible since all college problems are large. The reverse is true in the matrimonial venture. Invariably young love birds agree Mamma will settle all minor questions and Papa all major problems. Oddly enough, all questions are small the first year and by the time Papa begins to grow spurs Mamma has already reduced major problems to feminine questions.

Our own student government, like Topsy, sorta grew up. As a teacher, I was constantly searching for some practical system of instruction. Some aspects of social studies were thrilling enough to earn recognition by both boys and girls. The boys relived the careers of Francis Marion and his courageous frontiersmen. They became military strategists hunting out British redcoats with George Rogers Clark, or tramping through the snow at Valley Forge. Naturally, following Sublette and Fremont across the Rockies was more interesting than Western novels. What lad doesn't dream of trapping with Kit Carson and facing the dangers of mountain men. The exploits of Ashley and his gigantic fur trade made St. Louis a trappers' paradise. Geographic terrain was important because herein scurried the kind of fur-bearing animals sought by hunters. It also gave a clue to Indian tribes and skills needed by white men fortunate enough to escape their arrows. Interestingly enough, the Indians were not always dangerous. Many a trapper owed his life to their kindness. Without Indians, Ashley's intrepid hunters could never have held their immortal rendezvous.

These were actually huge market places. Indians and traders came from miles around. Here were furs, cloth, knives, guns, trinkets, and whisky. There was an exchange of possessions amid great feasting, drinking, and fighting. Horse races, gambling, and Indian women were features of attraction hard to emulate. When it was all over, the Indian vanished into the hills with his trinkets and the trader returned to St. Louis with his furs. Great stories were woven about these events that were relived by the boys.

The girls read and reread stories about glamorous Priscilla and the young swain, John Alden. They were willing to endure Miles Standish, the lovesick old warrior, in order to spin with the lovely maiden of Plymouth. A beautiful girl needed men to compete for her affections, even though one of them was too old for the race.

Pocahontas portrayed a phase of feminine devotion that stirred the sacrificial emotions of the girls. What woman doesn't dream of throwing her life at the feet of her courageous suitor? Pocahontas proved woman's superiority of men was prevalent even in the savage. It is a feminine quality that emerges to the surface when circumstances warrant her sacrificial gifts. A man will fight to his death, but a woman gives her life freely for the man she loves. The bravery and spirit of Pocahontas, exemplified in throwing herself on Captain Smith to shield him from the executioner's ax, was a realistic illustration of the fearlessness and devotion of women prevalent in every era.

Sacajawea has more of a masculine flavor than glamorous Priscilla or courageous Pocahontas, yet her trip on the Mississippi with Lewis and Clark carries a feminine dream buried deep in the heart of every girl. A curvaceous form was not a criterion for attention where femininity reigned supreme. Even a repulsive girl could be a glamorous queen traveling alone with an army of men. Although this Indian maiden was not repulsive, neither was she a beauty queen, yet her masculine adulation exceeded that of most women.

This phase of social studies held a certain amount of appeal for the girls, just as battles were interesting to the boys. The problem lay more in civics than history and geography. To distinguish between the powers of executive, legislative, and judicial branches was beyond the grasp of sixth-graders and only the periphery was touched by my eighth-graders.

Mike was never very good at memorization. He struggled enough with poetry, but the dry complicated lines of democratic jurisprudence was anathema to his soul. Mike was more interested in feminine lines than lines born out of the mental agony, groanings, and soul-searching theory of some eighteenth-century lawyer. He could remember the owner of petite feet tripping through the hallway far more vividly than the author of a federal document.

Mike was not the only student to wallow in the civil documents held sacred by silver-haired teachers. Even the Preamble to the Constitution, the Bill of Rights, and other fundamental documents were difficult enough to understand, let alone memorize. We struggled with memorization through devious channels and various associations, but sentences dangled and important words became blank spaces. Obviously, the signficance of the Declaration of Independence was lost in a mass of conglomerate words. The Constitution stumbled, faltered, and fell on its face. As for law and individual rights, they became disciplinary regulations beyond the comprehension of even the most brilliant student. The question before us, therefore, was obvious: "What could be done to clarify social studies with its variegated hue of social behaviorisms and geographical changes?"

We recognized its value, feared its expansiveness, yet were aware of a cohesive element that ran through each phase of man's relationship to man and the universe that encompassed him. How to put each element in its proper perspective was a super-human task. As a group, we attacked the course of study submitted by the county superintendent, which added spice to some portions that would have other-wise fallen flat. Here and there a pinch of illustrated beauty helped put life in otherwise dead material. We climbed the mountains of India, walked the Sahara Desert, viewed an Egyptian sphinx, and even courted Cleopatra with Antony, but to analyze the regulations that made all these events click was beyond our comprehension.

I explained to the combined seventh-and eighth-grade boys that certain clubs, classes, and schools were organized to help determine the policy of their group. This system had merit both for group direction and practical democratic information. If our school deemed it worthwhile, we could inaugura-ate a student council, court, and system of laws.

Clarence was first to express an opinion. "Our room varies in ages, and that might make it too hard."

Before he could continue, Milton doubled for him, "Clarence means the lower classes would feel funny trying to discipline our class." He continued, "But this isn't likely because fairness can make all the difference."

"I'm inclined to agree with Milton," John seemed quite interested because he was struggling with the organizational phase of social studies. "My brother says the student council in high school helps keep things organized for his school."

I turned to my seventh-grader, "What's your opinion of this venture, George?"

His words came slowly, "I don't know much about it, but trying to act our lesson might make it easier." He paused to think, "I'd like to try a student council because I want to pass."

It was my turn to express an opinion or, at least, make a more vivid explanation. "I suppose what we will do depends largely upon our needs and desires. Some states have a unicameral type of government which allows for one legislative branch. Others have two houses for legislative purposes." I paused to let this sink in.

Sometimes George surprised me with his alertness, and this proved to be one of those times. "Civics seems quite complicated to me," he said, "but I think two or three pupils would be enough for our lawmaking body."

This was good thinking and I said so. "George," I stressed his name, "sometimes you display a streak of rare wisdom and this is one of those times. In my best judgment, your suggestion has merit worthy of careful consideration."

Clarence came to life now. "If we had one legislative body of two or three pupils, would the executive branch be one person?"

"That's a good question, Clarence. Who has a better suggestion or a new idea to make our governing body complete?"

John, aroused from his slumbers, ventured a suggestion. "If this great idea is modeled after our national government, we need a judicial branch."

"I think we need two justices," Milton added. "One chief justice to hear a case and one associate to help decide the sentence. I doubt that any one pupil would want to sentence another."

"Good thinking, Milton," I agreed. "Now the question before the house is, do we want to accept our slate as presented or discuss it a mite more?"

"What have we decided?" Milton wanted to know.

It was my turn again. "As I understand it, George suggested one legislative branch with perhaps two members, Clarence thought one person was sufficient for the executive department, and you wanted two justices."

Milton arose to his feet. "Mr. Chairman, I move we accept this type of governing body with two legislators, one executive president, a judicial department, and the two upper branches known as the student council."

"All in favor of the motion say aye." There was a chorus of ayes. "The vote was unanimous, so the motion is carried. Now," I continued, "we'll have to formulate a constitution and present the completed document to the school. In my feeble judgment, you cannot force this on the student body, for its value lies in its complete acceptance."

The boys started thinking out loud. "It will take time to work out the details." Enthusiasm breeds activity and the possibilities of the project were taking root, "Maybe social studies will come to life if we work out our own system of government." They were still expressing their thoughts aloud, "It's likely these ideas will make more sense if we can live with them everyday."

It was my time to butt in. "I agree one hundred per cent, which means you will be wise to keep your school in mind as you define the duties of each department. I suggest you get a copy of our national Constitution and use it as a basis for your own. Once the branches are defined, you'll need certain rights that, obviously, belong to students of your age level. Then you'll need guidelines for disciplinary measures. The federal constitution might help at this point. When everything is finished, we'll present it to the student body for acceptance. This will be your lesson until the assignment is completed." With that speech, I dismissed the class and they went to work.

The boys thought this would be a snap, but two weeks passed before they had a definite plan ready for acecptance. It was read, reread, evaluated, and finally presented to the students for approval. By this time, it had become a popular subject and was accepted without a dissenting vote.

Election of officers created as much furor as a national election. It immediately became evident which families were Republicans or Democrats. Small caucuses met to nominate their candidates, and political techniques were put into action. Our school decided to elect the chief justice and his associate which added to the interest. As was expected, Milton became president, John and George legislators, and Clarence was chief justice with Gordon as his assistant. By this time, school was drawing to a close, so very little was accomplished beyond establishing the student council as a desirable organization in our school. Since the officers were all upper classmen, they added prestige to their positions. It was an honor to hold office, which meant everything was in favor of a successful student council for the ensuing year.

When school convened that fall, one of the first matters of business was the election of a student council. At least one phase of schoolwork had not receded into its shell of forgetfulness. The idea of self-government appealed to all the students. Bart, however, seemed more interested in the judicial rather than the legislative branch. He wanted to prosecute a criminal, at least insofar as we had criminals.

Bart probably expected to be elected to an office, but his enthusiasm never waned when Gordon was chosen president, Mike and George legislators, and Vivian chief justice. Julie was her assistant. Insofar as Bart was concerned, this election merely put the wheels in motion, so the next step was to find a law breaker and hold court.

The boys kept their eyes open for the slightest infraction of a rule, particularly by a girl. As was expected, Judy became the first victim. She was caught throwing chalk at one of the boys. She pleaded "not guilty," so the judicial department was launched on its career.

Bart volunteered to prosecute the case. Judy was called to the witness stand and given her oath by

Sharon, who had her place her left hand on a dictionary, raise her right hand, and take an oath. Sharon asked, "Do you swear to tell the truth, the whole truth, and nothing but the truth?" We omitted "so help me God."

Judy answered, "I do."

Bart began his questions, "Were you working at the chalkboard on the morning of September the twenty-seventh?"

Judy replied, "I can't remember."

Bart evinced consternation, "What do you mean, you can't remember? You know the girls in this school have special privileges and get to work arithmetic on the chalkboard."

Ruth, acting as Judy's lawyer, jumped to her feet, "I object. The question is irrelevant, circumstantial, and not related to the charge. Judy is not on trial for the teachers' attitude toward the girls."

"Objection sustained," Vivian intoned.

Bart was not to be deterred. "Do you know what time school was dismissed on the afternoon of September twenty-seventh?" he asked.

"Yes," was Judy's immediate reply.

Now Bart drove home his point, "Do you mean to insinuate you remember when school was dismissed but cannot remember your privilege of working arithmetic on the chalkboard? I suggest the teacher let you stay in your seat since you don't know the difference between your seat and the chalkboard."

Ruth was on her feet in a matter of seconds, "I

object. This type of questioning is designed to confuse the witness and has no bearing on the case."

Bart was sober as a judge. "Your honor, I intend to show that the witness does know whether she was working at the chalkboard on the date indicated."

"Objection overruled," said Vivian.

Bart pressed his point, "Was there any day last week when you worked arithmetic at your seat?"

Judy answered without thinking, "No, I worked at the chalkboard every day."

Now Bart had the upper hand. "September twenty-seventh was Thursday of last week; therefore, you were working at the chalkboard on the twenty-seventh, is that right?"

Judy gave a meek, "Yes."

Bart brought up his next point, "Did you throw chalk at Mike on that date?"

Judy's reply was an excuse, "He hit me with a paper wad."

Bart became insistent, "The question is not what Mike did. Did you throw a piece of chalk at Mike?"

"Yes," admitted Judy, "but he hit me first."

Bart had scored a point, so he merely said, "Your witness."

Ruth was not whipped, so she said to Judy, "Please tell the court just what happened on the morning of September twenty-seventh."

"I was working arithmetic with the girls," said Judy, "when Mike walked by to sharpen his pencil and pulled my hair. I kicked at him and I missed.

He took his seat and shot a paper wad, hitting me on the leg, so I threw a small piece of chalk at him."

Ruth was through and said, "I have no more questions."

With the dignity of a real judge, Vivian said, "The witness may step down. Next witness."

Bart was sure of his case and answered, "I have no more witnesses."

Ruth, too, felt the trial was over and said, "Let the case rest."

Vivian was not through, "Each lawyer may sum up the case," she said.

Bart had little to add, "Your honor, my case is clear. Judy was accused of throwing chalk and admitted the same on the witness stand."

Ruth made one more effort to free her client. "Since Judy was tormented by Mike and tried to protect herself with the most convenient weapon, she is not guilty of the charge. In the eyes of the law a woman has a right to protect herself from an assailant."

Vivian's decision showed a rare widsom seldom seen in an elementary pupil. "The evidence indicates Judy was molested by another person, but this does not give her the prerogative of taking the law into her own hands. Therefore, I find her guilty as charged, and sentence her to remain in one recess. Furthermore, she will write, 'I will not throw chalk,' one hundred times. Case dismissed."

It was a good trial and gave a realistic insight into jurisprudence not evident in dry reading. This was an actual case with punishment pronounced upon the guilty. Several cases came up within the next few weeks, then I called a halt because some trials took a couple hours or even more. These kids fought for their freedom to the extent of using me as a material witness.

Presidental elections were held every two months. Gordon had done a good job but declined to run again, so George succeeded him and remained in office throughout the year. George was a superb officer. He called the council together to arrange our Thanksgiving dinner, decided when to publish our school paper, put a committee on the Christmas program, took care of Valentine's Day, Easter, and all other activities in which the school was directly involved. I thoroughly enjoyed working with George.

I remember that on one occasion Vivian was up for trial for chewing gum during school hours. Our policy was to have a hearing of the chief justice before the student council. Vivian admitted her guilt. She had been chewing gum during the noon hour and forget to remove it when school reconvened. In pronouncing sentence, George explained, "Some of us try to observe the regulations as set down by our constitution, and those imposed by our teacher. Recognition of necessary disciplinary measures is a mark of good breeding, intellectual growth, emotional stability, and emergence into adulthood. I am aware, nevertheless, that those of us who endeavor to uphold the law can be at error because of forgetfulness, unusual circumstances, and unexpected events. In view of these facts, and your own exemplary character, I'm going to suspend sentence and admonish you to be more diligent in the observance of existing regulations and helpful when you see the rest of us in error."

It was a long speech for George, but characteristic of his thoroughness. He had developed a great deal in this last year, and it showed in every phase of his work. I'm sure he spent several hours preparing for Vivian's trial and the things he wanted to say. Classes have a great deal of merit, but few classes can accomplish what one trial uncovered in the life of a growing boy.

Before the year was up, Vivian resigned as chief justice and Gordon was elected in her place. Vivian and Julie were made legislators and were splendid help to George. Gordon was put on the spot one day when Bart asked for a trial in which Julie was the victim. She was accused of running down stairs and hitting Sam. The trial was insignificent. I usually punished such infractions by asking the guilty culprit to come back and walk. As for hitting Sam, that could have deserved some attention, but generally such things were passed off as playground events. This incident might have been forgotten had the girl been someone other than Julie. Julie, like Vivian, seldom did anything wrong, so the boys clamored for blood. I yielded to pressure, and Gordon sat in judgment over his favorite sister. Julie didn't contest the trial but pleaded guilty as charged. She made no effort to defend herself other than to say Sam called her a dirty name and deserved more than he got. Sam was brought before the bar and pleaded guilty. To sentence Sam and vindicate Julie indicated partiality. Gordon's face turned crimson as Bart, Sam, and the younger boys clamored for justice against Julie. Sam was willing to accept his punishment, providing Julie was given a stiff sentence. Julie looked daggers at Gordon, as if daring him to sentence her. Finally, in desperation, I said to Gordon, "You know it is not necessary to pass sentence at this time. You have a perfect right to pronounce sentence at a later date."

Gordon's relief was indescribable. He pounded the desk and said, "Court is dismissed until a later date, when it will reconvene to dispense with this case." Evidently the kids felt they overstepped their bounds, for Gordon never sentenced Sam or Julie. Other trials were held but these two were forgotten.

A number of things should have come up for trial, but we let them pass unsung and long forgotten. Take, for example, the day we were invited to the missile base. While listening to an explanation of missile control through a lighting arrangement, one of our pupils emptied his or her bladder. I saw a puddle on the highly polished tile floor about the same time our guide skillfully escorted us to another section bordering their restrooms. I guess he thought one major catastrophe was enough for that day.

On another occasion we observed field day by visiting the state university, then joined the multitudes to hear President Kennedy. As Lulu, who never seemed able to keep her clothes straight, was hurrying up the bleachers to find a seat, her petticoat slipped down around her feet and tripped her. I picked her up, pulled up the petticoat, and sent her on her way. Ruth lost her purse that same day. It fell through a crack in the bleachers and went far beneath to the ground. When the meeting was over, Ruth got on her hands and knees to see what had become of her purse. Just then an energetic girl dashed under the bleachers and grabbed the purse, but Ruth yelled so loud the frightened girl gave it to her.

One day Bart came in covered with grease. There was an old school building about one hundred yards from the new one. I had forbidden my pupils to go to the old building without permission. Bart's curiosity overpowered his caution, however, and he slipped off alone. Early that morning a group of vandals had stopped to vent their wrath upon something and smeared axle grease all over the old building. Large globs of grease were thrown promiscuously around on the inside landing, on walls, stove, desks, and floor. Windows were smeared both inside and out. The door resembled a grease bucket. Bart had to investigate the crime and returned from his escapade duly punished by his own curiosity.

I suppose the question of when and how to punish boys and girls for doing the inevitable will always remain an unanswered question. What do you do when a schoolhouse is built with every other brick protruding about two inches to form a ladder for scaling the wall? Any boy with a grain of adventure must climb that wall and walk around over the flat roof schoolhouse. Oh, yes, I forbade them to climb the wall but a ball can accidentally land on the roof, and it takes two or three boys to retrieve it.

If a teacher set out to punish every infraction of proper school conduct, he wouldn't have time for much else. Our school was conducted largely on the merit system and student discipline. Yet I noticed elementary boys and girls can become weary of ruling themselves. New situations arise that detract from student government.

In our school Gordon was nominated president the third year but declined to serve more than one term. Julie was elected to replace him. This made our governing body predominantly feminine. It was during this period the boys and I were sentenced to make up fourteen minutes we used one noon to clean the old schoolhouse. The boys felt the decision was made on prejudice rather than fact. I've always had a great admiration for Vivian, but realize a twelve-year-old girl could have swerved under the insistence of her classmates.

The girls vindicated themselves later. We were practicing for a softball game and our ball went to pieces. The students had a small fund they accumulated through craft work presented at the county fair. This fund was controlled by the student council, which was made up entirely of girls. Although they spent some time playing ball among themselves, they never expected to use a new, expensive ball. Nevertheless, when I asked for money to purchase a new ball it was granted without debate. Womanlike, however, whenever the boys insinuated the student council favored girls, they reminded them the new ball was strictly for the boys. Generally this money was used to supplement special dinners prepared by the girls and eaten ravishingly by the boys, at least, their share of it.

Student control is not a panacea for all ills related to schoolwork, but it helps in both disciplinary measures and scholastic growth. The boy or girl who recognizes a need for arithmetic, spelling, history, grammer, and other subjects develops a keener comprehension for fundamentals than the boy or girl forced to attend school. A dollar for each *A* earned by a student may have merit, but an *A* above the standards of achievement, attained through desire, stands the ravages of time. Student government amplifies the liberties necessary for individual effort and self-analysis. My pupils were better able to meet the challenges of life because they learned to meet the challenges of school. My aim was to let them experience life in its depth and not live on the periphery of childhood fantasies.

CHAPTER V

ART AND SPELLING

To better indoctrinate my pupils with the intricacies, beauty, and pressures of life, I taught art and spelling. Every school deals with these two subjects to some degree. The question is to what measure should they be meted out to the students? Art demands freedom of expression to blossom out into life and beauty. The student must become the flower, the animal, or the scene he is painting. He must emerge from inhibitions and yet learn to control his actions. He removes the protective shell that preserves childhood fantasies and gives full sway to the subject at hand. If painting a chipmunk, he learns to move, act, fear, fight, and scold like a chipmunk. Self unfolds and the chipmunk moves in all his peculiarities across the mind of the painter. The chains of antiquity are broken, and the student emerges like fresh fruit ready to be consumed by his art. Liberation of the soul brings a richer reward than domination of the mind. Accumulation of facts has its reward, but freedom of thought can win a crown of righteousness which the Lord, the Righteous Judge, will give.

Freedom of thought makes way for the appreciation of beauty. Once Vivian never noticed the many boulders she passed on the hillside, then she painted them with their various shades of color. Their drabness took on life, their ruggedness became strength, and beauty enveloped their cylindrical form. How easily we step over a common stone and miss its eternal splendor. As Vivian mastered art, drabness took on color and the hillsides were bathed in beauty.

Not many of us can distinguish between colors, primarily because we are not trained in color differentiation. The artist must be able to distinguish fine shades of yellow, brown, red, green, blue, and others. He learns to mix colors in order to produce a desired shading. Such ability demands practice. Detail work often becomes tedious in many fields of endeavor, but not for the artist who changes boredom into fascination and detail emerges from the mundane into an effervescent infinity. The clang of the hammer becomes the resonant tones of a baritone. The clatter of chains is transformed into the hallelujahs of an angelic chorus. Blending of color changes piercing sunbeams into a glorious sunset, or a dreary morning becomes a radiant sunrise. The artist can change defeat into victory, despondency into hope, shame into virtue, and sin into salvation. When Jesus, the master artist of life, saw a repentant sinner nailed to a cross, he said, "To day shalt thou be with me in paradise." The dark colors of hate were blended with the crimson colors of love, and death was submerged beneath life. Likewise, the boy or girl crushed by the mundane trials of everyday living is lifted to new heights and grasps the immortal threads of hope. A hope that is not shattered when the picture becomes dim, for the painter knows a dark blot can be made bright with a skillful stroke of his brush.

Before a student can reap the values of art, he must learn something about it. It takes a teacher familiar with some of the techniques of painting to teach painting. My knowledge of any type of craft was limited. Insofar as my abilities were concerned, painting was scarcely a craft. Clarence knew something about applying colors, Mike could draw coordinating lines, and Milton had some knowledge of wielding a knife. All my pupils knew a little about tearing paper to make designs. As for me, when I don't know anything, I'm screwball enough to try to find out.

My co-worker that first year worked with the lower grades and introduced them to all sorts of odd things such as crayon designing, a conglomerate array of pencil marks, silhouettes, wheels, squares, cylinders, dolls, and camels.

I collected models of carving, clay modeling, sewing, and even simple types of sketching. We tried drawing each other instead of attempting silhouettes. Frankly, the results were beyond recognition. John used me as a model and surprisingly enough his reproduction bore some resmblance to my homely features. It was the only caricature, that's what it actually was, we dared keep. John displayed his masterpiece at our school exhibit and won a blue ribbon.

My method of teaching was without precedent. In some rudimentary craft projects the pupils wisely ignored me and used their best judgment. As for finger painting, I scarcely knew what it was let alone how to teach it. The girls seemed to enjoy this messy job, so I let them continue until their desks, arms, legs, and clothes were an array of colors. Fortunately, water colors will wash off, so this project resulted in a few designs good enough for presentation. Frankly, what the kids learned in this field of artistic experimentation is still a mystery to me. Obviously they learned the art of getting water colors off their legs, arms, faces, and clothes but if anything positive was derived from this mess I was too dense to discover it.

We had a couple of projects that had some merit. About Christmas time I asked Clarence, "Do you think you and Mike could color a Christmas scene on the chalkboard?"

Before Clarence could answer, Mike chirped in, "We can all make the picture. Gordon can draw pretty good and all the boys can help."

"Mike's right," Clarence agreed, "I can make the general outline then everyone can fill in the background."

I handed Clarence a Christmas card of Mary, Joseph, and the Babe in a stable. "Do you think you could draw this?"

By this time all the boys were gathered around us and piped up, "Sure, we can draw it."

"We have a lot of colored chalk left over from last year," John said with a note of enthusiasm.

I looked at John and asked with a bit of irony in my voice, "What good will it do you. You can't draw and your writing is atrocious."

John's features never changed and his drawl was truly Western, "I thought I might make the hay. Loose hay is sorta messed up."

A smile creased my lips, "You have a point there." I added very seriously, "Perhaps you could do the donkey's tail. In my section of the country cockle-burs bunch them up into a glob."

Gordon chimed in, "I could color the nailheads on the manger," then hopelessly asked, "or did they have nails in those days?"

Mike, feeling his superiority to Gordon in this field, laughingly said, "You can make the hole in the cave." At this point Gordon clobbered him and the meeting adjourned.

The boys really worked on their picture. Clarence sketched an outline, then Mike added more details. Each boy asked Clarence what to do, and the picture soon took on a rich, rewarding color. Milton was so well pleased he brought his camera and took colored slides of both the picture and artists. We had the slides made into colored pictures and exhibited them at the county fair.

One major project in the field of art was a fort modeled after the type used by New England pioneers. I bought some quarter-inch dowel pins and was given a lot of quarter-inch strips of scrap lumber the lumberyard had left over from larger boards. These were cut into various lengths and used to make homes, church, town meetinghouse, corral, gates, and the outer wall. Posts on the wall were all shapened like a pencil, with the sharp end protruding upward. I was really proud of the boys, for this piece of work took us all year. It was worth the effort, however, for we won a blue ribbon plus the acclaim of many school officials.

The thing that really crimped my style was trying to teach oil painting. When our material was put beside that of a neighboring school in the district, we hung our heads in shame. I resolved to do something about it.

Not long after school began in my second year, the teacher whose pupils had good oil paintings stopped at my school. "I've got to figure some way for you to teach art to my pupils," I told her. "Your exhibit was exceptional for elementary pupils, and I want the same advantage for my students."

She was a short, buxom lady with a heavy woman's capacity for love. "I'll be glad to help in any way I can," she said, "if we can figure out a way."

I didn't quibble around about details but barged ahead. "Why don't you simply come over here and I'll go to your school?" was my suggestion.

She smiled knowingly, "You know that wouldn't work. I couldn't handle your boys and get anything done." She paused a moment. "I'll tell you what we might try. I'll bring my school over here and teach them art the same day I teach your pupils. The two of us ought to be able handle all of them."

"Your word is my command." I jumped at her suggestion. "I'll carry the club and you wield the brush."

Thus our co-operative venture was launched. Its success lay in the fact she hoped to gain as much as she gave. She had five girls, ranging from the first to the seventh grade who needed contact with other pupils, especially boys. We planned to work hard but we also took time for recreation and the social amenities.

Fortunately for my girls, her seventh-grade girl could paint better than my sixth-graders. This gave my girls both a challenge and faith in themselves. They all had as much native ability as her student. It was a matter of concentration and application. As for the boys, they could do anything the girls could do, that is, if they wanted to. Furthermore, they all wanted something to exhibit at the fair.

Although painting was work, it held a redeeming aspect for the boys. It was not study from the standpoint of using a textbook, so it contained a tinge of recreation. Even the hint of play was better than no play at all. They soon learned that it took our visiting teacher a long time to give each pupil individual attention, so all they needed to do was get stuck and wait for her. The only fly in the ointment was our decision not to dismiss for recess. Our school became a prison to the boys, but a measure of freedom could be gained by feigning weariness to ask for a five-minute reprieve that could be extended a little longer, particularly if the teachers were busy.

I enjoyed these days as much as the pupils. It was rewarding to watch them grow. Once totally ignorant of color combinations, they soon saw what a transformation could be made in a picture through the use of a properly applied color. Again and again a pupil would give up and say he wanted to quit, then Mrs. Brown came along, gave the picture a few carefully placed brush strokes, and the picture came to life. This was a lesson in more than color technique. It touched every subject in the school curriculum. How vividly a deftly placed stroke indicated victory was only the width of a paintbrush away. Other lessons could be the same. One more trial in a spelling lesson and all the words would be memorized. Another five minutes of study and a reading lesson would pass inspection. An arithmetic problem needed only one more trial. Social studies were conquered through persistence. This was life, whether in schoolwork, home frustrations, or social adjustment.

The trials of life were often hard for these boys and girls. Sometimes their days were overcast with black, foreboding clouds. They were through, washed up, whipped, then came the master's brush in some form and those clouds were transformed into a radiant sunrise. Here was a new day decked in all the glory and promise of joys untold. How quickly the drab became colorful, defeat became victory!

I watched each pupil change from hesitancy to courage. In the beginning they were like babies learning to walk, afraid to take a step. Mrs. Brown patiently told them what colors to use and where to brush. The girls were especially timid. These boys and girls lived in homes where each dollar was spent with frugality. To take expensive paint, valuable canvas, and high-priced oil out to the garbage heap was willful waste. It was better to be safe than sorry. Yet slowly but steadily they learned to venture out alone. After a year of experience I saw Vivian reproduce on canvas a waterfall with its huge boulders and roaring stream. Judy depicted a beautiful lake decked with trees and a partial fringe of rocks with a few giant stones scattered along the edge. Ruth ran a river through the rich underbrush of flat country. Julie portrayed a lovely hillside sheltering a cosy cabin. Sharon brought a lonely cowboy home on his faithful horse through a blinding snowstorm. These girls once stepped very lightly on the painted canvas, but now they took long skillful strokes and beauty emerged before their eyes.

Gordon received a lot of ribbing from Mike in the field of art, but Gordon saw the majestic Teton Mountains and portrayed them with the skill of an artist. He developed from a timid, insecure novice to a budding artist daring to try new lines and colors for effectiveness.

George had a talent for painting. He could discern colors in scenic pictures that bore a richness not evident in the average work of boys and girls. His lines were not always used to the best advantage, but he chose deep, rich colors to feature mountains, trees, and other scenic points.

Both Dale and Ted showed marked improvement, but Sam could try the patience of the saints. He had individuality but nothing more. I thought Sam tried to do what he was told. Mrs. Brown, however, thought he was indolent. Obviously something was wrong, because a mountain might be where a tree should be or a boulder in the middle of the road. The type of picture Sam really worked on was a portrayal of thoroughbred bulls. He was a born cattleman and tried to make a good painting of his favorite bulls.

When it came time to display our craft following a year of Mrs. Brown giving us periodic guidance, I was proud of our exhibit. It was the first year our school had ever shown so many oil paintings. Papas and mammas gloated with pride over the works of their offspring. These people had to watch their pennies, but they all managed to buy suitable frames to give each picture a proper setting. Mrs. Brown and I displayed our craft together. Not only did we have good material, but there was so much of it my room resembled a booth at the state fair.

One task was packing the stuff away. We put everything in big boxes and stored it in my room to be displayed later at the county and state fairs. Fortunately my responsibility ended at my school. What I needed most was some assistance in dismantling our carefully arranged display. The pupils had co-operated splendidly in putting it up; now, they were scurrying about hither and thither. I caught a glimpse of Ruth and said, "How about a little help in taking down these posters?"

Ruth stopped long enough to say, "Just a minute, Mom wants me to carry some food out to our car." Ruth disappeared into oblivion.

Gordon rushed past the door so I yelled, "Hey! Gordon!" He stopped for a breath of air, "I could use a good man right about now."

"I'll see if I can find one," Gordon shouted back. "I'd be glad to help but I'm just a boy. Anyway, I'm supposed to start cleaning the basement." He waved his hand, said, "Have fun," and was gone.

Just then I caught a glimpse of Sharon in the hallway talking to Judy. I stepped through the door, walked up to them, and said, "I have a nice little job, especially designed for two lovely girls."

They smiled sweetly, with false enthusiasm, and said, "We'll be happy to help you." Once in the room they asked, "What shall we do first?"

"Pack the paintings," I replied, "then get a box for some of these little articles."

It looked as if I had won. The girls soon had all the paintings down and packed away. Then Sharon said, "We'll have to go look for a box." Before I could reply, they were gone.

I continued to slave away, wondering when the girls would return to finish their job. Just at the point of exasperation, Julie and Vivian appeared on the scene and offered to help. Fearful lest they might be an apparition and suddenly disappear, I suggested they start packing booklets. About five minutes later my balloon was deflated again when Vivian's mother came to take her home and Julie went to look for Judy. Mike stuck his head in about that time, so grasping at straws I said, "Mike, come here a minute." He came in and I pointed to two rows of booklets, "See those booklets?" I asked.

"Sure," Mike answered. "What about them?"

"Nothing particular," I said, "I just thought you'd like to run a race. I'll bet I can pack the farthest row faster than you can pack this one."

Mike smiled wisely and said, "I know you can," and walked away.

I gave up. School was out and the kids, free of their shackles, wanted to flap their wings.

The art of success is more than packing various types of craft for display. It touches every phase of school life. I had a lot of trouble with Sam but that boy had an art for reading. He read his reading assignment like a professional. Social studies were easy for him because he read widely, especially in the fields of history and geography.

When Ruth first came to school her writing was wretched. I told her she ought to be ashamed of her papers. The girls took special muscular exercises and Ruth scrawled her lines. I wrote little notes explaining her errors and added suggestions for improvement. Perhaps the thing that helped most was my avowed dislike for good-looking girls who were despicable writers. I told the girls if there was anything that turned my stomach it was a pretty girl who didn't measure up in every other field of endeavor. Whatever did the trick, Ruth worked hard to develop a unique style of penmanship and her writing became an art.

Many students falter, stumble, and fall in the field of mathematics. I allowed a full hour to study arithmetic and often the boys and girls thought this was a long time. Perhaps it was for several of them. Sam struggled to keep up with his schedule. He would skip a few pages and claim he had worked all the problems. I'd test him out only to discover he couldn't work them, so back he went several pages. Between cheating and backtracking, poor Sam finally completed his book.

Ted, on the other hand, constantly surprised me with his grasp of math. He waded through problems like a duck takes to water. To Ted, the solution of problems was rapidly becoming an art.

We learned there is also an art in spelling. I'm a very poor speller and never got too excited about my pupils learning more than the required number of words designated by the school curriculum. My neighboring teacher, however, was interested in winning the national spelling contest. Naturally, some of her enthusiasm rubbed off on our school. One of the things we did on her visits to teach art was to practice spelling. It was from her I learned that spelling, like other accomplishments, is an art. There were definite methods and hours of study with slap-happy methods sandwiched in between.

When Mrs. Brown came over for art, we would divide our time so as to hold a spelling bee of some description. It might involve a spelldown of the lower grades, then, the upper grades. The boys might spell against the girls. Two pupils often chose sides for either a spelldown or a baseball game. Occasionally we wrote words, and checked for the highest grades. All of these methods were concomitant to unadulterated hard work.

Mrs. Brown's champion speller studied all summer. When school started in the fall, she spent many extra hours getting her regular subjects in order to get through, if possible, by Christmas. After Christmas she utilized almost the entire morning studying words. This was often done alone for a couple hours, then she would write or spell aloud a couple hours. Words were pronounced by her teacher, a fellow student, or a school patron. In this manner she learned a surprising part of the dictionary.

Words are learned by phonetics, suffixes, prefixes, root words, and by association. Often it was necessary to learn only one word and its derivation in order to spell a number of words.

One day following a spelling bee, I asked Vivian, "Do you want to be a champion speller?"

Her answer was immediate and emphatic. "No!" she said, and walked away.

It was evident none of my pupils wanted to study for the championship. In order to make a creditable showing, I told my sixth-grade girls to learn all the words in their bracket plus those in the seventh grade. That year Vivian won third place in the district, while Julie and Ruth tied for fourth. The next year I did the same, and again my girls placed in the district spelling contest. I have no quarrel with spelling contests but have a conviction that such rigid discipline is for the few rather than the many. A champion must work many long, grueling hours and have the co-operation of his school, home, and community. Training is valuable but a retentive mind is obligatory.

A champion gets very tired but, like the gambler, they get so near the jackpot they keep trying. Joyce had high hopes of winning the regional contest held between several states, but she failed to make the top ten. A week later she became state champion, which helped redeem her pride. When it was all over, I asked, "What are you going to do now? You're in the eighth grade and there are no more spelling contests."

Her unequivocal answer was, "I'm going to throw all my spelling words away and never look at them again. I'm so tired of spelling I'm sick of it."

My effort to console her got sidetracked in an elongated sentence, "I guess every champon gets a little tired, but after your spirit has been revitalized, I'm confident your reward will be a restful pride that, regardless of external pressures, will enable you to retain a comforting ego. In simple words, I suspect the reward is worth the effort."

"I suppose it is," she agreed, "but right now I'm sick of the whole mess."

A couple weeks later our two schools took a field trip, and Joyce had forgotten all about her long hours of spelling. She was a happy young girl who enjoyed life to the fullest.

Joyce won a ribbon but Ted deserved a medal. He advanced from an attitude of hopeless inferiority to one of achievement through application. When we held any type of public spelling match, Ted had wanted to crawl in a hole and cement a lid over it. It was embarrassing to stand before a school of good spellers and miss simple fourth-and fifth-grade words. It took several conversations before Ted was willing to accept his position in defeat. He would say, "Let me sit in my seat and study. I always lose for the side I'm on."

To which I invariably replied, "You are in school to learn, Ted. This is the place to make mistakes. You may be a loser now but you won't always be. Stay in there and keep pitching."

"I don't mind so much if you hear me miss," he would say, "but the kids laugh at me."

"They don't mean to be rude," I tried to be understanding. "They like you and want you to learn just as much as I do."

"You may be right," he'd say and take his place with the other spellers.

Ted was about a year and a half getting in the groove. I insisted he make ninety or above in his daily spelling lessons and constantly called his attention to misspelled words in his compositions. To look at Ted and listen to him talk, you'd think all my efforts were in vain. Underneath his veneer, however, was a driving desire to learn. At first my notes on his papers were so much splattered red ink, but gradually Ted, like the other students, learned to appreciate my notes almost as much as a good grade. Often my notes encouraged my pupils to try for a better grade. If their papers warranted poor grades, I simply indicated the necessary corrections and wrote, "Do this again." The girls long ago regarded a poor paper as double work. To them, anything less than an *A* was poor. Ted was slowly but steadily climbing to that same level of achievement. Once he thought in terms of passing. Now he would accept a two but worked for a one. He had learned the thrill of work well done.

Just as spelling and art became a boon for character development to the other pupils, they had a surprising effect upon Ted. Art demonstrated the asininity of despair, for with the proper stroke of a brush dark became light, drab became beautiful, and the mundane became eternal. Spelling demanded a tenacity that eventually bore fruit. Champions were not made through slipshod methods of study but by a constant systematic effort in unyielding doggedness. An impregnable wall could be scaled through perserverance.

Chapter VI

THE QUINTET SHOWS MAGNIFICENT
PROMISE

The girls enjoyed all their classes but few classes received a more wholehearted response than reading. At first they studied the entire story, then read certain portions aloud in class. In order to create greater interest, and diligence, we criticized each girl immediately after she read her lesson.

If a word was mispronounced, punctuation mark ignored, or wrong emphasis given a certain phrase, the girls would tear their classmate to shreds. I urged them to criticize constructively as well as to disclose errors. A good critic would detect both the good and the bad.

Criticism was practiced throughout our three years together, but its effectiveness was periodic. Even good scholars must have variation to maintain peak interest. This meant we had to find various ways of correcting mistakes and stimulating interest.

One day we completed an interesting story and Sharon asked, "May we give this story as a play?"

I was a little surprised. "I don't know, Sharon."

I glanced at the story. "The story is written for reading, not dramatic acting."

Vivian quickly added a solution, "We can use the conversation and make separate speakers."

"There are enough characters in the story for each of us to have a part," Judy explained.

"Who's going to write the script?" I wanted to know.

Now came the hallelujah chorus: "We'll all write it," they chimed in unison.

Even at this early stage of our co-operative venture in scholastic growth and character building, I could never resist the girls. Usually, I told myself, it was because their requests made good sense and helped broaden their scope of intellectual attainment. I suppose, however, like most men, I have a weakness for the feminine sex, especially when, like my girls, they were special.

They worked like little beavers on the play and came to class eager to demonstrate their dramatic skills. Actually the script was written more in the form of a pageant than a play. Sharon read the descriptive part and directed the stage setting. At times the characters were told when to appear and what to say. It wasn't a masterpiece, but it was a try and was produced without teacher direction. I praised the girls for their efforts and encouraged Sharon to spend more time at acting. "You have dramatic ability," I told her. "Perhaps you ought to put more effort in that field and see what you can do with dramatics."

Even in the fifth grade she was gracious and said, "Thanks, I'll try reading some short plays."

"What about me?" Judy asked. "Didn't I do a good job?"

"You, young lady, always do a good job. Sit down and I'll tell each of you what I think of your acting." They drew their chairs close to mine. "You all did surprisingly well," I said, "but not perfect. Sharon showed innate acting ability which might be worth cultivation. All of you had good characterization. Your trouble, Judy, is pronunciation. Both you and Julie chop off your words. I suspect it's an outcropping of your soft Spanish inflection. English has a full, resonant tone. Both languages are fine, and your Spanish background is commendable, but while you're in school, learn to give your letters a full rounded tone." I turned to Ruth, "Watch your speed, young lady. You run your words together. Just remember reading isn't a horse race. The characters in your play were all good, wholesome, American boys and girls who spoke and acted very much as you do when you're not in class. Class can make machines out of you. You did quite well, but try to make your characterizations more realistic and your pronunciation clear."

"May we do another play?" they asked.

"Later," I said. "Tomorrow read the next story and try to pronounce your words distinctly. Sometimes Judy reads as if she has a mouth full of mush. Sharon stops to analyze each word before she pronounces it. Julie and Ruth read the same words over a couple of times, and Vivian cuts the tail off many words. Try to read as if you were holding a conversation in a play. Now, scoot and get to work."

The element of time always seems to be a factor in schoolwork. In order to hear each class read, I had to cut their reading to a minimum. There was a tendency for students to assume they were ready for class recitation after glancing at their lessons, so I finally assigned a story to be studied and a short excerpt for oral reading. This had to be read with a minimum of mistakes or the pupil read at recess. In order to meet this requirement, the girls either went to the basement or huddled in a corner and read aloud to each other. Obviously, all words had to be pronounced correctly, which required the use of the dictionary and a knowledge of phonetics. Comprehension was cultivated by writing the story. They first wrote a long comprehensive review of the story, then, about Christmas time, there were a few short compositions. Later this changed to complete outlines with the use of books and finally brief outlines were permitted. Every student looked forward to the time he could hand in a brief outline, but these came after creditable work in the other phases of study. I felt the value of this system of study was twofold. First, the pupil learned the contents of his story, and, second, he learned both the art of written composition and how to outline.

The girls usually handed in comparatively neat papers, but occasionally they became careless and I ascribed a note which read, "The contents of your paper are creditable but your penmanship is sloppy," or, Judy, who was one of the worst transgressors, received this. "You're a mighty sweet girl, Judy, but your paper doesn't indicate it." Even after two years Julie occasionally hit low ebb, so I wrote, "A seventh-grade girl should hand in a neater paper than she did in the fifth grade," or, "Beauty is as beauty does," or, "The marks of adulthood are visible in the growth of the adolescent." There were many other notes, often dealing directly with the subject matter. A note to one girl was read by all five, so a correction on one paper meant a correction on all five. The result, of course, was better papers. Some of them elaborately decorated or purposely defaced their papers. Sharon might leave a blank space in a composition and write, "At this point my mind is a blank," or, she might leave a blot and say, "Whoops, my pen slipped!" Notes such as this would appear, "Do you know why a creamery employs blondes instead of brunettes? Be sure to read the next installment for your answer." Without an explanation, her next composition would have printed in bold letters, "It's difficult to see yellow hair in butter." I usually answered with some remark to add a bit of spice to our drab existence.

Reading and drama were so closely interlocked that we often used the reading period for dramatic expression. This was done in the form of plays and poems. Poems were a combination of literary interpretation and memorization.

As fifth-grade students the girls usually learned the poems in their readers. Some were quite simple. Yet they required careful study for correct interpretation. Memorization was sometimes a bugaboo. They first recited their poem to me for verbal expression, then wrote it. I never liked the singsong way many people recite poems, so I urged the girls just to tell me what they learned. They tried, but even after three years they had much to learn in expression. I do a commendable job of reading and went through many poems line by line, which seemed to help a little. In the latter half of their seventh year we read several poems and gradually caught something of what the poet wanted to say.

The girls learned to memorize their poems and insert every punctuation mark. I seldom corrected their work, as they were capable of deciphering their own writing and correcting it, especially with a copy of the poem before them. When corrected, the poem and grade were placed on my desk. I'm sure the girls were honest, because no finger of accusation was ever pointed at them. In the lower classes I might hear: "Lulu cheated."

Lulu would shout back, "I did not. Here's my paper, look for yourself."

Then came a howl from the boys in her class, plus another bark or two deep in the forest, "She has her book open in her desk, make her do it over."

Before I could answer, Lulu would assume a nonchalant attitude and would jest at their accusations, "Oh, you're all just jealous because you don't have your poems done."

The howl would become louder, "Make her do it over. We saw her lift the lid of her desk to copy."

I would hold up my hand and roar, "Quiet! Quiet!" After the children settled down I usually said, "I can't ask Lulu to do her work over on hearsay. You should have said something at the time she looked at her book. I have no alternative but to accept her grade."

They would reluctantly accept this verdict. It was unwise to press the charge, because they might be caught in a similar situation and want me to be just as fair with them. It's possible Lulu did look at her book a time or two, but she had aready repeated the poem to me in class so anything she gained was minute. The spirit of watchfulness was wholesome, however, because it kept the pupils alert. Copying was difficult with eyes watching from every corner of the room. Lulu, like the older girls, would soon learn honesty is best even though it might result in doing the job twice. My philosophy was that a student gained more by a second chance than when forced to make a good grade on his first trial.

Since poetry and plays are closely allied, the mastery of one is almost conterminous with the mastery of the other. A good actor must be able to interpret, and a good reader gives life to his words whether written in prosaic or rhythmic style. After many trials and errors, the girls gave commendable expression to both types of writing. Whether right or wrong, my pattern of teaching was an effort to unfold comprehension and expression in both poetry and prose.

In order to give my pupils a deeper appreciation of poetry, I read several poems to the school and gave them my own interpretation. To my surprise, Sharon gave me an unexpected compliment. She said, "I certainly like to hear you read poetry. Poems seem to have a message when you read them."

I cherished her compliment, for my girls were not given to superficial flattery. The only sane reply I could think of was, "I might read better than some people because I've had more practice. Then, as you know, I've had some courses in elocution. Good poetic expression takes a lot of study." I turned back to the class, "Frankly, I'm pleased with the progress shown by all of you. Julie has learned to pronounce her words in clear, resonant tones. Judy evidently swallows her mush before coming to school. Ruth has decided there is plenty of time, so she doesn't have to run a race while reading, and Vivian is reaping the fruits of her labors. You all know Sharon has her own unique way of reading, just as Ruth has a unique style in writing." My statement merely voiced a well-known fact, "I call it individuality. It can probably be developed into an enviable talent. Sharon, like the rest of you, has room for improvement which spells a lot of hard work. This satisfied their curiosity. Whatever faults I might have, one thing always stood out in bold array: my effort to criticize fairly and honestly was never doubted. I had taken the girls apart so often it seemed past time to get them back together again.

The girls had long ago learned how to sandwich a bit of solid thinking between gulps of humor and bantering. Class bantering was more than play-acting. It could be a release for pent-up emotions, or, beneath a flippant remark could be an immortal lesson. We broke up the monotony of work with play and augmented our play with study. Poetic readings were only one way to study. Drama was a definite part of our school curriculum. Usually it was studied in the form of play production rather than class recitation or spontaneous reverberations.

The girls carried their parts like real troupers in our various programs. They seldom complained about their parts and were diligent, untiring workers in both rehearsals and arrangement of props. We were a small school and many props were made by hand or brought from home. It took a lot of ingenuity to cobble up the necessary props.

Our great adventure was composing a Christmas play. We had searched through all available library books, but could find nothing that seemed suitable. Finally I challenged the girls, now seventh-graders, to write a play especially adapted to our school. Their first reaction was, "No! We couldn't write a play."

"Why not?" I asked. "You write many interesting compositions, many of which have long conversations."

"That's for class." Julie spoke her thought, "A play would be for our mothers and fathers to see."

"A play is for entertainment," Vivian added. "There wouldn't be much entertainment in anything we tried to write."

"Why not?" I asked. "Don't you take many of your compositions home for your parents to read?"

"I'd like to try it." Sharon was usually the leader in a new adventure. "How would we go about it?"

"I'm not sure." I was put on the spot. "It was just an idea that popped into my mind. Why don't you take a couple of class periods and see what you can do?"

"Why don't you write a play for us?" Judy wanted to know.

I gave this some consideration before making a suggestion. "First of all, I believe your parents would be more interested in your work than mine. Second, it would be good practice for you. If the play isn't good enough for production, we can ditch it. If, however, it has merit we can shape up the rough edges and produce it." I paused to let the wheels in my head turn around, then proposed a bright idea. "You write out all the suggestions you can think of and hand them in to me. I'll take your findings and make an outline of your most complete play. Each of you can take a main topic of the outline and develop the conversation. Then you can pool your results and put the play together, giving it cohesiveness. After you've done your best, I'll make such corrections and additions as seem feasible."

99

The play was written and produced at our Christmas program. The pupils thought it was a success, and since parents see only perfection in their offspring, they lauded their children to the seventh heaven. Perhaps this was not too important, because whether good or bad, the girls received a rich experience in play production.

The only really humorous event came in a serious scene. A little girl was to undergo an operation in the home of a pioneer family. In those days doctors used boiling water to sterilize their instruments, so our doctor stepped on the stage, after having examined the little girl and diagnosed her illness as a severe case of appendicitis, and said, "I'll need lots of boiling water." To the audience, this sounded as if he was getting ready to deliver a baby—not operate on a little girl. Naturally there was laughter instead of tears.

There is a close relationship in dramatics, poetry, reading, and language. The absence of one seems to lower the effectiveness of the others. Our language study inculcated many phases of intellectual growth. Sentence structure, composition, outlines, memorization, expression, comprehension, were all part of language.

As fifth-graders my girls went through their language book like a prairie fire. I had to digress to hold their interest. The sixth grade was almost a reproduction of the fifth. Compositions were written with skill, imagination, and expression. They mastered letter writing within a matter of weeks.

Capitalization, punctuation, word structure, and other grammatical techniques had all been studied in other classes. A short introduction to parts of speech was scarcely enough to tax their mentality. It took the seventh grade to throw an impediment in their forward march.

I had warned them that the seventh grade was a thorough baptism of grammar and would demand their utmost perseverance. They looked at me knowingly as if to say, "Sorry, old fogy, we mastered two years of language with time to spare. We hate to disappoint you, but we have no patience with skeptics. We'll walk through grammar and spend our spare time in some type of craft."

I saw the futility of argument and waited for the cloudburst. It wasn't long in coming. Simple subject, simple predicate, complete subject, complete predicate, nouns, verbs, adjectives, adverbs, modifiers, then, a group of one hundred sentences in which these were all to be segregated.

The girls came to my desk again and again with questions. Finally the sentences were all corralled and they were ready to correct their answers. I went through them one by one, looked up from the answer sheet, and asked, "O.K., what are your grades?"

Vivian smiled sheepishly and answered, "We flunked."

Now I was on top. "This stuff is hard, so I want you to do this lesson over. We'll check again and make sure you know why you put down a certain answer. We'll keep on this lesson until you know it before I give you a grade. Is that fair?"

The chorus answered, "Yes sir."

"Now," I said, "let's go over some of the sentences and see if we can discover why they are what they are." After several minutes of study, I asked, "Do you think you can do them now?"

Vivian, the brain, said, "I understand some of them. Maybe we can figure out the rest."

Sharon's answer was less encouraging, "I can't make heads or tails out of any of them."

"What about you, Judy?" I asked.

With a hopeless frown on her face, she answered, they're worse than a crossword puzzle; at least I can figure out some of the answers in a crossword puzzle."

"I'll tell you what, Judy," I said reassuringly, "You don't do anything when you get home but torment Julie, so you and Sharon stay in a couple evenings so we can study an hour, then I'll take you home. Would you like that?"

Sharon answered for her, "Sure, that's fine. We'll start tonight."

It was no snap and took several evenings, but we finally dissected, arranged, and tabulated the entire lesson. There were other portions as difficult, or worse, but the girls refused to be conquered. Once more they lifted their heads in the air and marched victoriously through every grammatical fortress.

The mastery of grammar added to the gradual perfection of schoolwork in its over-all perspective. Craft, for example, received its share of laurels. The girls made a number of articles that required a few weeks of skillful work. They were good, but I considered their social studies scrapbooks of greater value. They were the result of long hours of strenuous labor that extended over nine months.

An experience of Julie's is evidence of what it means to produce a prize scrapbook. One day she handed me a dozen sheets of paper splattered with water paints. Julie, usually very neat, had left her research work on the counter. Some careless pupil came along during the day, slopped some green powder from a can, mixed it with water, and let it slosh over the sides on Julie's papers. The tone of Julie's voice evinced her anger when she asked, "What shall I do with these"?

I took the papers from her and thumbed through them, noticing blotches of green paint on every sheet. I handed them back to her with this sage piece of advice, "Do them over."

She screamed, "Do all of this work again!"

Nonchalantly I asked, "Do you have an alternative?"

She came back to reality, looked at the green-stained paper, and said, "No, I guess not."

I tried to be sympathetic, "I'm truly sorry it happened, Julie, but it's done. There's nothing we can do about that. Even punishing the culprit would not change your papers. It's unfortunate, but I know of no solution except to do them over."

Julie, conscious of reality, tempered her voice and gave due credence to my position as a teacher, "I'm sorry," her voice was soft and feminine, "I realize you aren't to blame." She shuffled her papers. "Actually it won't take long to rewrite them and I'm sure I can make them much neater." She recognized there was not much use to cry over spilt milk. An unfortunate accident had damaged her possessions but, like a practical adult, she accepted her misfortune and tried to improve her lot.

This spirit was evident in each of the girls. They met defeat with victory, sorrow with joy, and loss with achievement. Most of the girls had younger brothers or sisters and knew the imperfections of human nature. The pathway of life was strewn with boulders large enough to bruise your toe. Occasionally, when not alert, you tripped and fell. Their road was not paved with gold. A poor painting had to be retouched, a poor composition rewritten, a soiled scrapbook cleaned and corrected.

Besides an accumulation of factual material, scrapbooks cultivated a filing technique. Some system had to be devised whereby material collected at the beginning of school would be neat and presentable at the close. A blue ribbon was given for neatness, arrangement, and creativeness as well as the accumulation of material. The girls were furnished folders but designed their own filing system. By the close of school their material had been collected and their scrapbooks were ready to be assembled. They made lovely covers of various designs. Usually the amount of work and originality of their arrangement warranted a blue ribbon.

Occasionally they became so engrossed in a project that they ignored recess. Because physical fitness is an asset which must not be ignored, quite often at recess time I would ask, "What do yo want to do"

The boys would say, "We're going to play football." Later in the year it might be basketball or softball.

Occasionally I'd ask, "Why not play touch football and let the girls play?"

If the girls wore jeans, they might consent to play with the boys. More often, however, I got this answer: "We don't want the girls. We want to play tackle."

Probably one reason for the boys' strenuous objection was their inability to beat the girls in touch football. This hurt their pride. Ruth was developing into a good athlete and could outrun all the boys except Gordon. Vivian could catch either the football or softball better than most of the boys. Julie was a pretty good pitcher, so regardless of the sport these girls held up their end of the score and indirectly shamed the boys. The only way for the boys to maintain their dignity was to let the girls play their own game.

Actually the girls were good sports. They knew their own ability and tried not to embarrass the boys. We played one game called "Darebase," in which they really tried to win. I played with the boys and usually managed to lead my team to victory. The game started with one team, with a base about fifty yards from the other team, touching their opponents' baseline and running back to their own base. Ruth always got opposite me and usually caught me. I had a feeling she did this for personal emulation as much as game strategy. Regardless of the motive, I was put in the girls' jail until rescued by a teammate. Once out of jail, I could usually remain free and direct my forces to victory. The winning team had to put all of their opponents in jail. Like most games, however, it was periodic. Few such games could hold their interest more than a week or so.

Generally we played outdoors. The kids always seemed to work better after a brisk ten or fifteen minutes of vigorous physical exercise. As the girls grew older, they leaned more and more to indoor exercises. During the winter different types of dancing became a fad. The boys seldom danced, because dancing alone was sissy and dancing in couples meant they would have to touch a girl.

I'm not sure how this girl-shy attitude started. When the girls were in the fifth grade, we played several party games that were enjoyed by the boys. By the time they reached the seventh grade, the boys loved them and were loved at a distance.

In the fifth grade we taught square dancing to the entire school. None of the boys evinced any shyness for these lovely fifth-grade girls. There were times when stalwart eighth-grade boys danced with petite first-graders. The older boys with a little girl did not create a problem. It was during this period that we presented several square dance numbers for the county music festival. Dressed in their red and white checkered shirts and blue jeans, the boys were almost as picturesque as the girls in their white blouses and flared checkered skirts.

It took some doing to get the awkwardness out of the boys. The girls, generally, were quite graceful. At first Judy threw her feet out like a pacer. Deborah jumped around like a bullfrog. Patty, a first-grade Negro girl who looked like Topsy, bobbed her shiny pigtails up and down as she bounced like a rubber ball. The stars were Sharon and a lovely first-grade blonde.

The boys shuffled around like a fat man on ice, so I said to the other teacher "Something has to be done. These guys even walk like an old cow."

"You don't need to tell me," she answered. "The question is what can we do."

I stuck my fist under my chin to meditate, then suddenly out popped an idea. "Some years ago," I began, "I remember young fellows would walk down the street in step with their girl friends. Often this required dainty little steps for a long-legged man." I paused for breath. "The point is they did it." Now if we lined the girls up along the wall and started them walking across the room and made each boy catch one of them and walk in step with them, it might help. The girls could take big steps, little steps, walk fast or slow, and the boy escorting her could change his pace accordingly."

She turned and shouted to the girls, "Get in line over by the wall." Then to the boys, "Line up over here on the stage. You know," she said to me, "this might work." Once more turning to the school she issued directions, "I want the girls to walk along the wall to the end of the room, then turn and come back to me. I want the first boy to catch the first girl, take her arm, and keep in step with her regardless of how she walks. The next likewise following in succession. O.K., let's go."

Well, believe it or not, this experiment was a success. Our awkward boys became graceful gentlemen and made our dancing exhibition a great success.

The girls were anxious to continue dancing the next year, so I bought a couple of new records and we learned two new dances. There were times when the boys objected to dancing, but I insisted they needed this type of training for rhythm, social grace, and poise. It was obvious this year to even the novice that the girls far outshown the boys. The novelty of something new had long ago worn thin, so we gradually lessened our dancing periods. The third year saw almost a complete halt to mixed dancing. This year the girls were young ladies and the boys still boys. It became a cardinal sin to touch a girl, so I endeavored to observe the sanctity of boyish pride.

One day Sharon asked, "Why don't we ever square dance?"

My reply was, "You know the boys. You know how awkward they are on the dance floor."

She remembered our first year and asked, "Why don't you make them walk again like you did before? They could learn to keep in step?"

"It's possible," I told her, "but you know Ted and Dale. They are growing fast and their feet flop around like bell-bottom pants on a windy day. Another thing," I continued, "our boys are in the gang age, which means girls are an anathema to them. They are taboo, especially you girls, because you are young ladies whose actions and thoughts are more adult than juvenile. They love you, but don't want the other boys to know it."

"I hadn't thought of that," she said, "but now that you mentioned it, I guess you're right." She paused a moment, "It might be just as well to forget dancing with the boys. We girls can periodically take the records to the basement at recess or noon." She looked at me with the wisdom of an adult, "I guess we girls still have a lot to learn about men."

"Perhaps," I answered, "but probably not as much as we men have to learn about women."

She started to leave, then turned to express a new idea, "It just occurred to me that in spite of boyish prejudices against touching girls, we might revive some interest in the square dance."

"I'm listening," I said.

She continued rather slowly, as if forming her thoughts as she spoke. "P.T.A. is always looking for program material to liven up their meetings. Why don't we offer to sponsor a square dance? There are enough pupils to show the adults what to do."

"You have a point there, Sharon. Daughters could dance with fathers and sons with mothers. We might give it a try." She smiled inimitably and left.

I told all the pupils about Sharon's suggestion, and they were all for it. To them the night was months away and crept along at a snail's pace. Time, however, never stands still, so the climactic hour arrived in a couple of weeks. Even the parents looked forward to it with keen anticipation, but were quite reticent to step out on the floor for a partner. We decided on the Virginia reel. This required two lines each facing the other. In our situation some of the girls became men. To start things off, I used four pupils who carried their parts like professionals. Next came two adults with their student partners. Fortunately, my pupils were willing to lead the dance and guide their partners at each turn.

Well, it was a lot of fun, particularly for the bystander who watched little girls lead their giant fathers through the dance routine. My job was to push lumbering men and fat bouncing women around so they wouldn't get lost in the melee.

Parents, primarily mothers, were occasionally invited to other functions arranged by the girls. As early as the fifth grade, they planned, cooked, and served dinners. In the fifth grade I watched them quite closely to see that the potatoes weren't ashes or the soup didn't scorch the floor instead of bubble in the kettle. We tried several meals that first year, with much of the food brought from home. The girls made out a menu and asked each family to bring certain things such as pie, cake, vegetables, rolls, pickles, etc. This year the teacher and I bought the meat. The girls set the table, and when everything was ready, called the rest of the school. I had them all line up, and Sharon led them in singing grace. They marched by the serving table, then took their places at the table. At this time my young teacher was helping, so she watched her little darlings and I held a club over my hoodlums. In this manner, things were kept comparatively quiet. Now and then a boy decided he wanted a second helping and started to get up but I barked at him, and he waited to be served. Thus we had a certain amount of decorum and noisy kids became little cherubs.

The next year we held our first dinner on Thanksgiving. This year Grandma, who taught the lower grades, didn't trust the girls alone in the kitchen. She decided to help them prepare the meal. Well, Grandma worked all right but succeeded in getting only a minimum amount of work from the girls. When the idea of another dinner was mentioned, Ruth asked, "May we girls prepare it by ourselves?"

"Why," I wanted to know, "didn't you like your Thanksgiving helper?"

Now they all spoke. "She wouldn't let us do anything and we'd like to cook the meal ourselves."

My reply received a little deliberation since it involved another teacher. "If you had a dinner for our room alone, or, invited the lower grades instead of holding your dinner jointly, I imagine it would be your own program and you could plan it as you pleased."

My dejected pupils were immediately transformed

111

into enthusiastic girls anxious to try their skills. "Thanks," they said, "let's get a paper and work out a menu."

"Hold everything," I reached out to grab the closest girl. "You'd better decide what you're going to do. Is this a one-room project? Is it an invitation dinner? If the latter, you'll have to plan for the entire school and furnish the meal." I paused for emphasis, then continued, "What about your mothers? Do you want your mothers to come?"

Judy spoke up, "I'm sure our mothers would like to come."

"It would probably be best to invite the lower grades. Sharon spoke slowly, as if considering the wisdom of her answer, "Actually, this wouldn't matter much because most of the pupils are our brothers and sisters."

"What's the verdict?" I wanted to know.

Vivian and Julie were in a huddle, so I waited for their suggestion. "We think it would be nice to invite both the lower grades and our mothers." Vivian was the spokesman. "Not many mothers will come, so any added preparation would be insignificant."

"If this is agreeable to everyone, I guess you're ready to plan the meal. Be sure you use good judgment in determining the amount each family should bring." I knew they would plan wisely, for unlike Grandma I trusted my girls.

There was no domestic science class in our school but my girls were learning some of the techniques of

112

culinary arts. Some of the boys whose manners were grab before the other fellow does were learning to wait, recognize God as the creator and sustainer of life, and even absorb a little of the cultural advantages of proper etiquette.

It would have been much simpler to let each pupil bring his lunch than prepare an all-school dinner. I might have had less criticism from some of the parents, but I wanted my boys and girls to meet life in its variegated colors. Even our classwork touched on the fringes of new adventure instead of following the well-marked, humdrum road of yesteryear.

The girls, for example, earned privileges not generally accorded the other pupils. Those students who worked diligently, didn't make unnecessary noise, and mastered their lessons, could study downstairs. This meant they could talk freely and work without the supervision of a taskmaster. Different groups were allowed this privilege, but few of them could earn it. Even though I permitted many small groups to go downstairs, invariably only a few could remember that freedom from the teacher did not mean freedom to play. The girls, however, coveted their freedom and were seldom reprimanded for misbehavior.

Such an attitude made school life a pleasure. True there were times of vexation and implementation of rigid discipline. On one occasion Sam assumed an authoritative attitude that grew worse by the day. This was contagious, and pupils began to talk about pulling pranks undetected by the old man. Ruth told her friends some of the stunts they pulled downstairs. Then one day they came to school and I put a vise on every move they made. They marched into the classroom, stood at attention by their seats until I said "Be seated." No one whispered or left his seat without raising his hand to ask permission. They were as quiet as mice. At recess they stood around and whispered. When noon came they marched out, got their lunches, and returned to eat without comment. That was Thursday. Friday was a repetition of Thursday. That evening just before school was dismissed, Ted held up his hand and asked, "Will we still run a penitentiary next week?"

Very calmly I answered, "That depends on you. If you don't appreciate your freedom, you certainly aren't going to get it."

Now the ice was broken and all hands went up. "We want our freedom," they said, "we don't want a strict teacher."

"We'll see," I said and dismissed them. This was the only time I ever had to use severe discipline. Actually I think it was good for the girls because Ruth was getting a little indolent. Generally, however, our school was free, pleasant, and enjoyable.

Field trips helped to break the monotony of textbook perusal. They were more than a natural application of class information. Instead of running off like jack rabbits, the girls watched the younger children and helped them profit from the trip. For their dependability and co-operative spirit, I offered to take them to the Denver museum. Their enthusiasm was evident in this question, "What time shall we start?"

"How would seven A.M. suit you?" I asked.

Ted, who was in the same class with the girls, groaned, "You mean to be here at the schoolhouse at seven in the morning?"

"Sure, isn't that all right? That's just an hour earlier than I come every morning."

"Yeah, you can make it O.K.," he faked deep concern, "but how will I get here, walk?"

"Yes," I agreed, "I used to walk three miles to school every day. You run all over the hills anyway, just run toward the schoolhouse."

Ruth jumped into the fray, "He's just talking to hear his head rattle. He can either stay all night at the store or he can walk there and come with us."

"What about me?" Gordon had to get into the discussion with his two cents' worth.

I had an answer for him, "I'll be around for you at six-thirty, young fellow, and you better be ready."

Sharon and Vivian, who were always ready, asked, "What time will you stop for us?"

"Why don't you get ready by six-twenty? I might be a little later but it will be about that time." I didn't need to worry about them. For that matter, I didn't need to worry about any of these kids. By this time Ted had become a fine dependable boy. That's why I was taking them on this trip. They had all worked hard and earned a vacation.

Once the day arrived and we were on our way, the kids started bantering each other. They anticipated a full day of pleasure with a minimum of scholastic growth. This was a school day for most schools, so when we passed a group of kids on their way to school I said, "Look at those poor unfortunate boys and girls."

"Yeah," Ted tried to add a symapthetic note to his voice, "I'd sure hate to be in their place."

"You're right," Sharon agreed, "maybe I should throw a kiss to the boys to cheer them up."

The idea must have appealed to Gordon because as we passed a lonely blonde, he stuck his head out the window and shouted, "Sorry, honey, we all have to suffer school sometimes."

The girls grabbed Gordon by the nape of his neck and jerked him back. "Don't make us look like a bunch of idiots," they shouted.

He setted down, folded his hands and, in a solemn, pontifical tone, asked, "What are we?"

Vivian's reply was no less sedate, "We're cultured young people on our way to a museum to increase our intellectual acumen."

Before she could add anything more, Ted shouted, "Whoa! This is a vacation; don't get so high and mighty."

Thus the bantering continued as we sailed merrily along the highway. A few times Ted became obnoxious in trying to force his attentions upon Sharon, but, generally it was a great day which the kids would long remember. There were many other occasions that broke the monotony of classwork and made school life a pleasure.

The girls would get their lessons and utilize their spare time in some sort of creative work. They liked frills and parties so we planned a few major festivities.

Halloween, for example, was a time of spooks and goblins. Grandma, the lower grade teacher, didn't like the idea of anything touching the little darlings' mouths. Nevertheless, we fixed a spook house with cat eyes, olives were used, the old witch's brew, a concoction mixed with plenty of mustard and pepper, worms made of spaghetti, and other delectable foods. When a victim came into the house, he heard chains rattle, ghosts moan, stepped on a dead cat, and numerous other attractions designed to scare the wits out of anyone brave enough to enter.

The spook house was only one game conceived and nurtured by my ingenious herd of primates. The boys insisted we dunk for apples. I bought some large apples and broke off the stems. Ted brought a large tub and filled it three-fourths full of water. The only way to get an apple was to shove it to the bottom or against the side of the tub and sink your teeth in it. As chairman of the committee, Ted said, "I'll get my apple first, then you can all line up and take turns." Ted took a deep breath, stuck his head under the water, and came up with an apple in his mouth, "O.K.," he said, "next."

Gordon followed Ted with the same success. Two more boys took their turns and mastered the feat. Now came Sam. The water bubbled, and he came up spitting and sputtering. "Come on Sam," they all cheered him on, "go down to the bottom." Again Sam plunged into the water but every apple eluded him. Once more coming up for air, Sam took a deep breath and went down determined to get his apple. The seconds ticked by and it looked as if he would fail again. His lungs began to ache but he refused to give up. Desperately, he shoved an apple against the side, covered his head completely with water, and emerged triumphantly. "Hurrah for Sam," shouted the kids. For fear that his experience might discourage the fainthearted, I took off my tie, unbottoned my shirt collar, and dived for my apple.

Now the girls wanted to try their luck. Ruth, like a thoroughbred bird dog after a duck, retrieved hers without mishap. It took a couple trials for Julie who, although small of bone, was bold and wiry. "O.K., Judy," the peanut gallery shouted, "let's see you do your stuff."

Judy pulled her hair back and went down, but the apples bobbed away like rubber balls. She would come up sputtering, wipe the water off with a sweep of her hand, and dive again. Finally Ruth said, "Let me get an apple for you, Judy."

The kids roared, "No! she has to get her own."

Judy was just as determined and blubbered, "If I can't get my own, I'll do without."

Sharon touched her shoulder and Judy looked up. Sharon carefully brushed her wet and straggly hair, "Why don't you let me dunk for my apple, Judy?"

Puffing and spitting water, Judy said, "O.K., but I'm going to get my apple or drown."

Whether Sharon couldn't get her apple or failed in an effort to encourage Judy, remains a secret. Like Judy, she went into the water until her face, hair, and shoulders were sopping wet. The kids yelled like football cheerleaders. The boys offered to drown themselves to get Sharon an apple but she, like Judy, could be very determined. Finally Sharon decided to rest and Judy took another plunge. This time she was successful, so Sharon stood alone. Could she follow the example of Judy? "Come on, Sharon," the kids shouted, "go down to the bottom." Everyone was crowded around the tub as Sharon filled her lungs and went down. Air bubbles floated with the apples as air escaped from her lungs, but she stayed down and shoved an apple to the bottom with her mouth and came up with a large ripe apple between her teeth. She had scored a victory and a loud cheer rent the air.

Christmas was a happy time with songs, games, and exchange of gifts, but Valentine's Day seemed to hold a bit of spice not evident at any other time. We had the usual candy hearts and routine cards expressing friendship and love. Canned expressions of affection bring a tingling sensation to both young and old, but my pupils designed their own cards and coined personal notes of affection.

When Sharon wrote, "Roses are red, violets are blue, honey is sweet, and so are you," it meant a lot more than the same note printed on a card. Ted would say to Sharon, "Tomatoes, apples, plums, or brew, none of these are pretty as you." Julie coined for Dale, "Sam likes ripe red melons, Dick likes yellow squash. Bill likes dill pickles, but I like you, by gosh." Judy gave Dick a card that read, "Some people work for gold, others cattle and land, but what I want on Valentine's Day is the arm of a real he-man." If there was any hatred or embarrassment, it vanished on Valentine's Day and love reigned supreme.

Love was always prevalent in our school, but expressed in devious ways. A boy might let a girl use his pen. She might let him copy an article she had looked up for social studies or help him in grammar. Little deeds of kindness often expressed reams of personal affection. When the girls sang on television, the rest of the school went to the home of a school patron to see them. There was a great deal of unexpressed pride evident for any pupil who excelled in any phase of school work. The girls earned their praise through hard work.

It was in the realm of music that Sharon proved a tremendous asset to me. She had studied enough music to play a few hymns. In other studies I cajoled, pushed, begged, and helped her to keep up with the other girls. In music, however, she worked untiringly and became the teacher.

Actually, we began our musical career in voice. "Sharon," I called her to my desk one noon, "we need something for county choir. We've used tonettes and dancing. What I would like to do is have a girls' chorus. It would take a lot of work and I'd need your help. Do you think we could do it?"

For the first time in weeks her enthusiasm bubbled over, "Oh, I know we can! I'll work real hard and do anything you want."

I looked at this lovely girl whose sweet co-operative spirit amazed me in one so young, "How much music do you know, Sharon?" I asked. "I'll have to depend a lot upon you."

"I play for junior Sunday school in our church," she said.

This is good but pretty amateurish. "What I'm thinking, Sharon, is considerably more advanced than Sunday-school hymns. I thought in terms of a woman's quartet book. You would have to learn all the parts and teach each girl her particular part besides playing the song. Can you do that?"

She never hesitated. "I'm willing to try. I could practice at home each day after school."

"You've had enough music," I reminded her, "to know it would be a long hard pull."

Her smile was captivating, "I know, the girls will get tired but I like music."

"Young lady, I believe you have what it takes. I'll get a book and we'll give it a try." I could see she was very happy.

Our first effort was to place the girls in their correct categories. Sharon learned, "Whatever Will Be Will Be," and sang each part for the girls.

Our first guess was an error. We gave Ruth and Julie second soprano and Ruth muffed her part by singing so loud Julie was only a figurehead. Judy was a perfect first soprano. She had a high sweet voice that trilled on the high notes. Ruth was switched to first alto, with Vivian and Sharon taking second alto.

Day after day we put each girl through her paces. For a couple of weeks they bungled their notes and the project looked hopeless. Sharon patiently sang with first one girl, then the other. As long as she sang they did fairly well, but when she stopped singing they immediately got off key. Finally I suggested each girl learn to play her notes on the piano. This took another week, but they began to feel their way so we put the parts together. It was pretty rugged. These girls were trying a completely new field and needed time to find themselves.

Trying to pick out their notes on the piano led to another level in music. Now they wanted to learn how to play the piano. "Do you know what this means?" I asked.

For a moment they were quiet then ventured a reply, "We know it's a lot of hard work."

"It's more than hard work," I assured them. "It's repetition of simple note arrangements over and over again. It was not long before you played songs with your tonettes, but this won't be true on the piano."

They were less hesitant now, "We know all of that. We're willing to work hard."

I looked at them with a love that transcends all scholastic barriers. They were sweet girls, eager to venture beyond the known into the unknown and uncover whatever hidden talent they might possess.

"Judy, you and Julie come to the city about every Saturday, so this week stop to see me and we'll buy a beginners' piano book. Then Monday morning Sharon can take each of you fifteen minutes during your reading period. We'll try this for a while. Sharon can take Monday to correct and guide your playing, then, you can each take fifteen minutes every day. This will be a slow process but it will be steady, so I think it might work."

Julie spoke for the girls, "I don't know much about piano music, but Judy and I will go with you this Saturday to buy some. We've decided we would like to take as much piano as we can."

"I think the girls will learn real fast," Sharon added, "I'll do my best to teach them all I know."

"They'll learn all right," I agreed, "but not very fast. You should practice at least an hour each day and they will have only fifteen minutes."

The plan worked exceedingly well. Sharon enjoyed her part as a teacher and studied almost as much as all four girls combined. Sharon was the only girl with a piano in her home. She assigned a lesson on Monday and checked the girls on the following Monday, which meant their rehearsal time was one hour for the week. The process was slow but rewarding. They soon learned their notes and could play their particular parts in the song they were learning to sing. One purpose of learning to play was to supplement their vocal music. Piano was taken during a portion of their reading period but singing was thirty minutes at the regular music period.

Far too often the girls had to sing alone. This was not always satisfactory, for, although they were diligent little workers, they were short on detail. Sometimes I'd leave a student in charge of the other pupils while I listened to the girls. This had as many flaws as there were pupils, because if one didn't shoot a paper wad another lambasted the student in charge. Nevertheless, we made commendable progress, and the girls were ready when the country choir was held. Dressed in white blouses and black skirts, they were five lovely girls whose sweet soft voices were a credit to their school. They had learned enough in this year of vocal and instrumental music to establish a good foundation for the next year.

In our second year of special study we launched out on the same general plan devised the preceding spring. Sharon worked with the girls each Monday in piano and I worked with all of them in voice. This involved considerable adjustment, as I had a new class studying tonettes. Some days I'd spend all the class period with the girls and other days with the other students. The result was commendable.

The girls sang for a few special occasions, including our county teachers' luncheon. We also prepared a couple of Christmas numbers. It was about a month after Christmas that we decided to work up a television program. I checked at the broadcasting station and arranged for a fifteen-minute program, about ten of which would be singing. Now I was forced to spend more time with the girls because they needed a lot of rough places smoothed out. Fortunately, my daughter, who was a fair musician, consented to help drill them each Saturday morning.

Saturday rehearsals really became a pleasant time. The girls came to our home at an appointed time and when the last one arrived I'd say, "Let's get in a huddle and get going."

At our first trial we scarcely got started before my daughter asked, "How did you practice this song?"

"I don't know. Why? What's the matter?" was my foolish question. Obviously everything was wrong.

My daughter, aware of my musical ignorance, said, "Listen to the tune while I play it through."

We listened and I asked the girls, "Do you have it?"

"I think so," Sharon answered for them all.

"O.K., then," I said, "let's go." The piano started, and they tried to sing but it was awful. "Hold it," I shouted. "We aren't getting any place this way. Why don't you gather around the piano like we do at school and give it a try?"

It worked. The girls caught the melody and their voices rang out in clear, pure harmony. After about an hour of almost continuous singing, my wife announced lunch. Since this was the first time the girls had ever eaten at our home, they were quite reserved. I noticed the table was set with a couple forks and spoons at each plate. These girls came from large families where one good fork was a luxury, so they were unfamiliar with two. After we were seated and had the blessing, I noticed the girls hesitated to eat. They whispered slightly to each other and looked at my daughter. Obviously they were embarrassed with so much silverware. To ease the tension I said, "What's the matter, Judy, you look baffled?"

She smiled sort of sheepishly and said, "We don't know which fork to use."

"You don't have anything on me," I chuckled, "I don't either, but I don't plan to sit here and starve for the want of a fork."

My daughter spoke up, "Never mind him, just eat your lunch." She paused and picked up a fork. "Generally you use the first fork for salad and the second for your meal. It doesn't matter here, so just enjoy your lunch."

I looked at Judy with a twinkle in my eyes, "Don't embarrass me. I'd hate to have my family find out how little you know."

Sharon was alert now, "Oh, we won't display our ignorance. We'll watch your daughter, not you."

"A rare piece of good judgment," I alleged; "on a few occasions I have been known to be in error."

"Yes," my daughter acquiesced, "perhaps it would be more correct to change the word few to many." This brought a howl from the girls, and our meal became a pleasant, festive occasion.

From this time on, it was never difficult to persuade the girls to practice on Saturday. We appeared at a special dinner soon after that at which I was the presiding officer. The girls sat together with my daughter, who accompanied them. They sang their numbers, ate their meal, and left. The next day I asked Judy, "Which fork did you use first?"

Before Judy could answer they all poured out a

conglomeration of words. "We weren't sure what to do so we watched Hazel (my daughter) and did what she did."

"I hope you didn't embarrass me," I assumed a serious expression, "after all, I presided at the meeting and you were my girls."

"Oh, we didn't." Their sincerity was mingled with enthusiasm. "It was a lot of fun though. It was the first time we ever attended an affair like that."

"Well," I droned, "just so you behaved like young ladies instead of young imbeciles."

Sharon's musical tones rang out, "We really felt like imbeciles, but actually I think we were very well mannered."

My heart reached out to these girls in fatherly pride. "I know you were well mannered, gracious young ladies. I received a lot of praise on both your appearance and your singing. I'm really proud of you."

"We're kinda proud of ourselves," Judy added as they went out to play.

Preparation for television was work but a pleasant kind of work. I put the girls through their paces both with and without the piano. One day Judy was struggling to get her high notes and asked, "Why do we have to practice a cappella? We'll use the piano on television."

"Because, young lady," I grabbed her cheeks in both hands and held her face up toward mine, "you sound like a flock of blackbirds each chirping his own song. If you have to listen to each other maybe, just maybe, you'll eventually develop a small degree of harmony."

"I just wondered," she said, "I didn't know my question would set off a first-class lecture."

I was just as presumptuous. "I thought it would take a thorough explanation to penetrate your cerebrum."

She bowed in humble submission, "Your descriptive phrases were quite adequate, most honorable teacher."

"Thank you, most gracious student." I too bowed low. "Shall we continue our instruction?"

Sharon butted in, "Please do, kind sir, and shall we omit the comedy long enough to sing?"

"Get your tones," I barked as I struck the piano. They each hummed their particular parts and harmony reigned supreme as they sang their hearts out.

As the day approached for their television program, there was considerable bantering among the students. Ted, always anxious to gain Sharon's attention, mockingly asked, "What are you going to do when that mug of yours breaks the camera?"

Ruth answered for her, "None of us will come as near breaking it as you would with your big mouth."

"How about Judy's spindly arms and legs?" Sam wanted to know. "They won't show on the screen. She'll look like the trunk of a tree."

"What will you do with beanpole Ruth?" Dale laughed and pointed to his victim. "If she stands by Julie you'll have a post leaning against a telephone pole."

"That won't matter," Ted yelled. "Fatty Vivian will cover up all the cracks."

"Maybe you guys should sing instead of us," Julie barked. "One thing for sure, all the television sets would be turned off and people would save on electricity."

It was time to voice my feelings so I said, "The big problem as I see it is not so much how the girls will look as how to arrange for you to see them."

"Oh," they howled, "who wants to see those clowns?"

I ignored the disdain and continued, "You might walk to Gordon's home if you were real careful on the highway and promised to be perfect gentlemen in his home."

All hard things already spoken were forgotten. "We'll be good, you can trust us."

"Gordon will have to take charge and you'll have to obey him," I said.

"We will," they shouted and held up their hands, "scouts honor."

The television program proved to be a success. The girls wore their white blouses and black skirts. Yes, they were nervous but no more than at other times. For fear that they might forget the words, I typed them on a sheet of paper that Sharon held behind Judy. Actually, I don't think they ever used it. Once more my daughter was persuaded to play, which gave them greater confidence because they knew she would carry them along if they got lost.

When it was all over and the girls had visited the

projection room, we went to the car. Their first question was, "How did we do?"

My reply was indirect, "The director on whose program you sang said you did a good job. In fact, she said any time you wanted to sing again to just let her know."

They digested this and concluded, "We must have been pretty good if she invited us back."

"I'm sure you were," I agreed, "but we'll soon know because the boys listened, you know."

This blew a fuse. "What will the boys know about it? Even if we were good they wouldn't admit it."

"You shouldn't be so hard on the boys," I said, "after all, they took time out to hear you sing."

"Time out to hear us sing," they exclaimed, "They took time out from their studies."

"Speaking of studies," Julie's voice emerged above the others, "let's stop at my house so we won't have to get back to school for another hour or so."

"It's a pleasant idea, Julie, but now that your television debut is over you'll have to study for a change."

"Do you mean to insinuate," Judy tried to be debonair, "that Holloywood stars should study?"

Sharon was solemn and deliberate, "We've followed your ideas this far with some degree of success, so if you think there is merit in studying textbooks, perhaps we ought to try it."

Yes, these were my girls—full of wisdom and wit. They had reached a pinnacle in music but there were other peaks to climb, so we hurried back to their books and more work.

It was not long before I arranged a radio appearance and made a recording of their voices. The peak of their singing, however, came at the county choir. I insisted they sing a cappella this year. At first, they put up a vigorous objection, but my logic prevailed and they consented to try. It took hours of practice. I had them go over special parts again and again. Words had to be clearly pronounced, phrases emphasized, and harmony perfected.

Since the girls had been on the air and sung on special occasions, the audience was ready to criticize as if to say, "Lets see them do their stuff." Well, they did. I had drilled them over and over but they never sang as perfectly as they did that day. Their pronunciation, harmony, timing, volume, expression were all good. I sat behind two teachers who turned to me when the girls finished their song and spoke in awe, "They were perfect. I never heard that song sung with such beauty and expression."

Some weeks later, the girls were singing at a special program and were asked to sing, "Beyond the Sunset," their county choir number. They had measured up to the highest expectations of their most severe critics.

It is not often a teacher is privileged to work with a small nucleus of students all equally congenial and mentally alert. They were average girls who came from ordinary families. Their genius lay in their pleasant attitude and co-operative spirit. Their ideals reached perfection and their efforts matched their goals. My task was merely to guide them in the expression of their finest characteristics, enable them to attain a richer comprehension of the world about them, and challenge them to utilize their talents.

Chapter VII

A CANTANKEROUS SCHOOL BOARD

The glow of teaching can be dimmed by bellicose parents or the members of a cantankerous, egocentric, litigious school board bent on breaking the spirit of any teacher foolish enough to enter their district. Their stoic officious decisions stand unyielding like the laws of the Medes and Persians. It is in the presence of these autocratic despots that a teacher must bow and scrape as a peasant before a medieval squire who may extend a scepter of peace or send him to the guillotine.

Like a lamb before the slaughter, I came under the sledge hammer of such a school board. In many respects the members were characteristic of all rural school boards of this enlightened era. The president, a short, rotund railroad man, received a small stipend for past services, so obviously he kept a roving eye on rising taxes. The clerk was a tall, angular ranch-man whose chief concern was to sparkle in the political limelight. The third member of this trium-virate had the temperament of a bull moose and the physique of Goliath. Under the guiding wisdom of this scholarly trio, I began a tenure of teaching destined to enlighten me in school board antiques if not instructional perfection. Fortunately, the latter two lived some distance from my school and were generally too preoccupied with other matters to interfere with the disciplinary measures of my school program. The president looked in often enough to make sure no unnecessary funds were being squandered on anything other than the bare necessities. The district furnished books, paper, pencils, and other things needed for general educational development, which meant that all purchases must be sanctioned by these mental wizards.

The obvious question arises: Why get involved with such screwballs? Why accept a teaching position in hades when there are unfilled vacancies in heaven? I suppose the simplest answer is a counterquestion, "Why did you marry a devil when there were so many angels walking the streets of your city?" This is an odd world full of peculiar people. As a minister I met a great many people caught in a web of confusion that they never dreamed of entering. The road to frustration and despair is paved with roses, but the road to happiness and peace is full of jagged rocks and piercing thorns. The road to hell is smooth and wide and many there be that travel thereon, but the road to Paradise is narrow and rugged and few there be that find it.

It was difficult to visualize my school as the golden fleece of Jason. The fact that I applied late in the year for one of the few remaining vacancies was already three strikes against me. The county superintendent, however, painted a glowing picture of a new brick schoolhouse built especially for me. Even as we talked about the many advantages this position offered over other positions, the president of the board walked in and greeted me with the warmth of a long lost friend. I was just the person needed for their unique situation. The Almighty had guided our steps to this office at this particular time. Divine providence had already chosen me, and the president was here to place his seal of approval upon a union consummated in heaven. My background as a minister added prestige to the wisdom evident in my hoary hair.

As far as the school was concerned, it was beyond a teacher's highest dreams. There were three eighth-grade boys whose mothers had expressed an urgent desire to have them pass with honor. A seventh-grade boy possessed a spirit unsurpassed in humility and untiring diligence. Two sixth-grade boys had been attending school together since early childhood and were encouraged by religious parents whose zeal and co-operative efforts added a plus to good work for their children. Then there were five lovely girls whose angelic wings had already started to sprout. Here was a great opportunity for character building and intellectaul growth. No one was better fitted to accept this challenge than I was with my solid character, enveloping love, and sound religious faith.

Being a man would add to the effectiveness of my command. Their former teacher was an elderly woman who lost control of her pupils, particularly the older boys. They were all good children and a stern hand would make this an ideal school. Once the pupils recognized that their teacher's authority was unbending, the battle was won and victory would be sweet. These boys and girls were not delinquents, just ordinary children who needed a guiding hand.

It began to look as if I was a privileged teacher, for this school was the cream of the crop.

Well, they didn't stop with ideal pupils. Here, also, was the finest building in the county. I was offered a new, modern building with tile floor and all the conveniences of a city school. The board had just bought a new sixteen-millimeter, sound movie projector, slide and filmstrip projector, record player, microscope, maps, and globe. These were all new this year, waiting to be used by a wise teacher. Obviously I could be that teacher.

Not only were there ideal pupils, a superb building, and new equipment, but other needs were available simply for the asking. What teacher in his right mind could turn down such an opportunity?

On top of all the advantages already mentioned, the district employed a bus driver and a custodian. The same family did both jobs through devotion to the school rather than necessity. They were the third generation of a courageous pioneer family and owned much of the land in that vicinity. Their primary motive in accepting this responsibility was to render a service. Both the husband and wife could drive, and the entire family cleaned the building. They were fine forward-looking, middle-aged people and leaders in the community.

This was the picture flashed before me in a few minutes. It was an unusual opportunity for service in an ideal setting. Although schooled in hard knocks through church squabbles, I was still gullible when under pressure and confronted with a pretty picture. Naturally, I accepted a contract.

The fine co-operative spirit of the school board was soon questioned by my young co-worker who had taught in a large city school system. She attended the first P.T.A. meeting and decided it was a farce, with no purpose other than to afford an excuse for a community gathering. It soon became apparent that the community was a dual setup rather than a single unit with one purpose.

When the P.T.A. met in our school a few loyal families attended who held some tinge of official authority. On alternate meeting dates, it assembled at the new Redrock school, and this community came out in droves. Few, if any, of our good patrons went to Redrock. It was soon evident to my co-worker and me that there was a definite line of demarcation between the two schools. Two other schools in the district were left on the periphery and could go or come as they pleased. Neither was expected to do anything or receive anything.

The P.T.A. served as a clearinghouse for school board procedure. Matters of special interest to one or more parents were presented to the P.T.A. for consideration. When they infringed upon holy ground of the triumvirate the matter was dropped with a word of admonition to the divine trinity that they take it under careful consideration at their next meeting. Teachers, however, were hesitant to speak of anything related to school needs. This might infer that there were imperfections in their hallowed school system. Imperfections had to be in the teaching staff, not the district's technical advisers and economic experts. These people were alert to the latest innovations advocated by the county superintendent, who weighed her position against their purse strings and emotional responses. I probably would have done the same thing had it not been for my stubborn streak.

Having run my own show for a quarter of a century, it was a bit awkward having someone else call the signals. As a result, I often carried the ball alone. Occasionally the president ran interference for me, but his boldness was not always in accord with the wishes of his teammates. It was, however, an asset to me and enabled me to reach some of those lofty goals painted so vividly at our first meeting.

It was at the beginning of my third year that the bubble broke. A teacher in one of the smaller schools was told that her services were no longer needed for the efficiency of that school. In order to make their suggestion more emphatic, the board hired a young girl to replace her. Most teachers probably would have been convinced the board intended that she look elsewhere for a teaching position. This woman, however, was unable to interpret sign language and stayed on the job. Her husband, loyal to his last shotgun shell, told the young teacher, the school board, and all other interested persons to stay off his land. Well, this squelched the new teacher idea conceived and promulgated by the board because the school house was on his land.

In the midst of this unsavory situation there were a number of heated discussions which, at times, seemed rather ungentlemanly. The railroad wanted to keep out of any questionable decisions, so quietly but emphatically asked their man to resign as president of the school board. This left my side of the district void of a representative on the holy triumvirate. How it would affect my school only the future could tell.

The young teacher spent her time in other school matters and the stubborn teacher took over her brood. Even Goliath had no special desire to dethrone her at the point of a sixteen-gage scatter gun. My primary concern was the replacement for our president. Would the new member's interest center around his home or reach to the four corners of the district?

For the previous two years I had noticed that residents near Redrock were not especially concerned about our school. The new board member was in the Redrock community; in fact, all three magi were now on the other side of the fence. Since it was nearly fifty miles to my school from their abodes, these gallant knights of the round table would need a representative, or a go-between. Whether they chose the bus driver, or he chose himself, is of little consequence. Officially or otherwise, he felt divinely inspired to keep our school properly supervised.

I had no bone to pick with the good brother, but one Friday evening after our first year of teaching together was in full swing, my young partner asked, "Are you going to clean your chalkboard this evening?"

I was not sure what she was driving at so I merely said, "I've already erased them fairly well and dusted my erasers. Why?"

She was more pertinacious now. "When I accepted this job, I signed a contract to teach school not serve as custodian. It's bad enough to sweep our rooms each evening but to serve as scrub woman is a little too much."

Although new at the teaching game, I felt she was justified in her gripe. "Why don't you leave your chalkboard and see what happens?" I suggested.

Evidently her mind was already made up because she snapped right back, "I intend to do just that." She calmed down a degree, "It'll be a consolation to know how much to expect from the parents of my prize pupil."

"Don't tell me you're already crossing swords with our community leaders?" My shocked expression bore a bit of irony.

She was quite demure. "I may not be here next year, but I plan to teach school this year. I've already made Master Sam aware of this, and evidently he informed his mother because her attitude toward me is coated with a thick layer of ice."

We had started to tread on dangerous ground, but I was sure this teacher knew how to keep her mouth shut, so any emotional outbursts would splatter out against the four walls enclosing our gripes. My comments, however, were pretty much within the scope of common knowledge. "His older brother probably thinks of the eighth grade as adult work because he gives me very little trouble. My major problem with him is how to cram a few facts inside his thick skull."

Even at this early stage of our teaching venture, she chuckled at her own reply, "Don't brag, next year, friend Sam will make up for any invidious pranks or slothful work overlooked by his brother." She paused for emphasis, "Then you will have the privilege of dealing with his infallible mamma and papa."

Now it was my turn to josh. "With persistence, maybe you'll have both Sam and his parents educated by the end of this year."

Unfortunately she didn't succeed in this mission. Although I must admit that she tried hard enough, she lost her job. I matched wits a couple more years with Sam before my demise. This was one of those situations in which parental lobbying was quite effective in driving teachers to greener pastures. A school board weighs the gripes of a permanent family against the merits of a temporary teacher and rules in favor of the school patron.

Many situations arise to tax the patience of good school board members, if there are any such creatures, and drive them to difficult choices because

141

both may be good yet only one can be accepted. To the teacher, however, it seems that the choice is more often worse or worst rather than better or best. I felt the worst interpretation often prevailed.

Since my board members all lived on the other side of the district, they absorbed doubts, skepticism, and suspicion. Once I could buy school necessities, but now every item had to pass through the office of the county superintendent. I needed a piano. I made a request at the beginning of the year, but the year passed without a piano. Blasting near the schoolhouse shook the ceiling tile loose, so I finally took a Saturday to repair it. The toilets caused trouble, I became the plumber. Our well did not furnish enough water, so I hauled water. The yard was covered with weeds and rocks. I held a cleaning day. Books were at a premium so I had several students work together in an effort to save money and educate my pupils. In order to provide lumber for craft work, I invaded the lumberyards for scrap lumber. I needed tools, so I bought some of my own and wore them out in school work. The girls needed songbooks, which were brought from their homes. To get them ready for television, I brought them to my home to use my piano, as it was difficult to sing on pitch with the piano falling apart. But perhaps the greatest thorn in the flesh was the board's suspicion that I favored one group over another and was letting some pupils slip by; furthermore, my classroom had supposedly become a roughhouse for hoodlums. Gossip filtered through the keyhole with a push from Grandma and the board gobbled it up like buzzards on a three-day-old carcass.

Obviously, the question foremost in my mind was, "What about the future?" If a cantankerous school board drove one teacher from her school and constantly added new restrictions to my schoolwork, the future looked like a dark cloud about ready for some type of devastating deluge. The wise teacher might "get" while the "getting" was good.

Chapter VIII

MY DEMISE

Sometimes it takes me quite a long time to realize that there is something brewing in the pot. Maybe it's because I consider myself a good teacher and think everyone else should feel the same. Oh, I'm not perfect, but I've worked directly with people over a quarter of a century. I've studied general psychology, pastoral psychology, sociology, guidance, and dipped into clinical training. I'm rather calm under pressure and have a reasonable understanding of, at least, elementary subject matter. Generally, I know as much or more than most of my students. Yet, dissension arose behind my back, and I had to be knocked down to see it.

The family that kicked over the traces always seemed congenial enough. We had met on numerous occasions and enjoyed a pleasant fellowship. The idea that they were dissatisfied with my teaching was as far removed from me as the East is from the West.

The school, insofar as I could determine, was moving forward at a creditable pace. As teacher and pupils we enjoyed many pleasant study hours, recitation periods, and vigorous recess activities. I was rather proud of my success as a teacher. Most of my students were ahead of their course of study, and had a commendable grasp of their subject matter. As for the disgruntled family, I had put forth extra effort in their behalf.

Their eighth-grade boy was slow in a number of studies, especially arithmetic. In order to correct this deficiency, I offered to tutor him each morning before school convened. The boy seldom missed his early class, so we made sufficient progress to keep him abreast of his class. This was extra effort on my part, so I assumed that this effort was appreciated by his parents. But apparently, the family felt degraded because their son had to have added attention. Anyway, a couple of years later my beneficent effort backfired, and I landed outside the district.

It's difficult to always know how to deal with mammas and papas. Periodically I had helped two other boys whose families sought out a gracious way of expressing their deep appreciation for my extra efforts. It seemed only logical to believe that the ruling monarch would respond in like manner for the added plus I gave his son, but apparently cattle kings have their unique pride.

It is quite possible I made a mistake in telling the boy's father that he was largely to blame for his son's low grades. The boy was able to make good grades, but seldom rose to his highest potential. This was obviously true at home, where he was overshadowed by an older brother who received all the laurels bestowed upon the family. My schoolboy had lived in the shadow so long that it never occurred to him he could accomplish something on his own merits. My suggestion was that the father recognize his younger son's potential and encourage him to do his best. No boy would strive for first place as long as he was expected to come in last. Well, it was a good speech, but, evidently didn't help my position as a teacher. People, especially those who like themselves, resent being told they could be in error.

This lad was one of the boys I worked with in preparation for the county music festival. His grace on the dance floor was comparable to that of a fat cow shoved out of a truck onto a chute where she would waddle down into the barnyard. Obviously he needed an inspiration, so since he liked Sharon, he was asked to dance with her. Her grace and poise gave him an incentive to manipulate his left hind feet a bit more to the gee side and to walk comparatively straight. A couple dozen trials more or less did wonders for this boy, and he performed beautifully at the festival. Since his parents didn't like the young teacher in charge of this event, they should have given me some credit for success. By all outward appearances, all the mammas, and the few papas who attended, were happy as an old hen in a corn crib.

I thought my first year was a success. In fact, I was inclined to agree with the school board president. This was a good school. These little hellions just needed an understanding teacher. Evidently, the president thought I filled the bill because a new family moved into the district that summer with two delinquent boys whom the president sent to my school instead of to Redrock, which was just as close to them. The president told me quite frankly that he thought I could do more for them than the other teacher.

There was talk of another district opening a school that fall but the decision was made against it because the parents wanted their children to attend my school. These things indicated that my work, on the whole, was satisfactory.

In order to make up for my deficiency in art, I arranged for a neighboring teacher to come to my school, periodically, and teach art. This was easily arranged because I could either go to her school or she could bring all her pupils to my school, and we both taught during the day. Regardless of how a particular day was arranged, it added up to the same number of teachers and pupils, so neither school was the loser. We both felt there were certain advantages to this dual relationship because my pupils profited in art and her champion speller was given a greater incentive to work toward her goal. If both of these subjects became tiresome, we switched to music. Music was quite popular in my school, so her girls were inspired to put forth a greater effort in that sphere.

In my school the girls and Gordon showed marked musical advancement. Friend Sam could neither carry a tune nor learn to play a musical instrument, so I let him tag along like the caboose on a train. I had a faculty for developing what I had to work with but I was not a magician sufficiently skillful to change a pickle into a watermelon or a monotone into an operatic star. It would have taken an even greater magician to change Sam, the ranchman, into a musician. Fortunately, however, there were a few things he could do.

Generally, where his mouth was concerned, Sam stood at the head of his class. He was given a major part in a Christmas play and stole the show. His parents had a right to be justly proud of him. I'm sure they were but some parents are not satisfied with one achievement. If Rastus excels in music, football, basketball, debating, spelling, or any other achievement, their son must do the same. Some boys are good, but few reach the mark of perfecton set by proud parents.

One assiduous side to my work as a teacher was my reception into the P.T.A. By the beginning of my third year I was one of the peasants. When asked to arrange a program, I did so with very little fanfare. The good people decided to sell candy, and I bought more than my share. This was my community. I had become one of them and conversed rather freely with the patrons on both sides of the fence.

I was unaware of a canker sore spreading over the district and boring its way into the marrow of my community friendship. The first inclination of trouble came one morning when visitors asked to see me in the corridor. One was a tall angular board member and the other a short squatty member who had recently been appointed to that hallowed office. It was the first time either of them had ever been to see me during school hours, and I was halfway through my third year. Both brethren, however, seemed well informed about my work as a teacher.

First of all, I was told that a new school policy had been adopted which prohibited a teacher staying in one school more than three years. This certainly knocked me for a loop, because I was on the home stretch of my third-year lap. Obviously, they were informing me I was through, done, washed up. They were gracious enough to assure me, however, I might be considered for a position in one of their other schools. I later learned they were willing for me to teach where the husband of a school marm held all encroachers at bay with a shotgun.

Once informed, that when the flowers decked the prairie my services would be terminated, I asked the reason why? This foolish question simply showed my ignorance, because they had already explained the new policy formed and adopted by the board. If I couldn't understand a simple explanation, obviously I wasn't a first-class teacher.

To further prick my good humor, they said some complaints had arisen about my discipline and my ability to teach math. The boy I helped during those early morning hours did not turn out to be a genius in high school. The inference was that since I had had the kid one year out of eight, the fault was all mine. As for the disciplinary matter, I pleaded guilty as charged, because my policy was one of student correction and honor. I interfered only when necessity seemed to warrant it. I challenged the good brethren to check my school's scholastic record and prove this policy to be unsatisfactory. Frankly, these accusations stirred up my ire, so I thanked the school authoritarians for their information and went to my room to start mulling over plans for my departure. I had no doubts about my ability to secure another school.

One disturbing question was, "Why the note of dissatisfaction?" I nosed around a bit and gradually gathered scraps of gossip that were probably as reliable as the gossip that brought the magi to my schoolhouse door.

For one thing, an influential family was disgruntled on several counts and my co-worker kept smoke signals rising every day. The coat episode in which my boys were accused of throwing her innocent darling's coat in the snow was only one of many affairs that brought her wrath down upon my hoary head and her mouth to the telephone. The latter was more fatal than the former. Hot words flowing to other widow and spinster teachers were really dangerous. Then, too, a rather unpleasant atmosphere often prevailed in her room which encouraged her cherubs to carry tales of woe home to their papas and mammas.

I tried to work with this battle-ax, but more often our personalities clashed in bitter combat. While I recognized her efficiency in the classroom and she could appreciate my problems, we just could not hit it off on a more personal, friendly level. If there had been other teachers in the school, our differences would probably have been minor; as it was, we were often like two snapping turtles in a small, stagnant pond.

Like many schools, we had a variety of disturbing things to keep the pot of discontent brewing. Occasionally it boiled over, but generally there was just a slow bubble, like the mud pots of Yellowstone.

Grandma was not the only one with elephant ears and a mouth with an automatic clapper. As anyone who is connected with the teaching profession knows, bus drivers see all, hear all, and know all. Ours was no exception to the rule. At times we had three drivers, which added to the rapidity of broadcasting school gossip. Kids usually understand their own rash statements about a teacher or an event, but when dressed up in adult trimmings, they can become infallible facts. I suffered the results of these fanciful ideas.

One flower that wilted away to reappear as a prickly thorn was art. An equally dangerous branch from this stalk was spelling. A neighboring teacher excelled in both of these subjects and, on several occasions, gave me some very able assistance. In fact, my students displayed some very fine paintings and made a commendable showing in spelling. This was fine, with some of my patrons, but was not adequate. The logical conclusion of these good people was, "Why receive this help second hand? Why not kick our teacher out and bring the good one over to our school? Our school could then have champion spellers and exhibit blue-ribbon artwork." This was good logic. Since the neighboring teacher taught alone, and no other teacher or bus driver caught notes of discontent to elaborate upon, the idea seemed flawless.

One little item which they overlooked was the school in which this teacher taught. She had a community solidarity that was welded together through years of toil and sweat. No one knew better than the teacher that what she accomplished in her own school could not necessarily be accomplished in mine. She had excelled in spelling. I surpassed her in vocal music. My difficulty lay in the fact that I enabled the wrong students to excell in music. You have to play the right cards if you want to stay in the card game.

This idea was expressed quite fluently one day by Mrs. Brown when we were talking about the new policy adopted by the school board. Both of us knew the policy was inaugurated in order to get me out of the way and force her into my school. "Are you coming over to corral my bunch of hoodlums next fall?" I asked.

She looked at me with the same disgust that was evident in her voice. "You know the answer to that question. About the second day I'd knock young Sam across the room and his papa would jump down my throat. I can't stand the way that kid hunches up and quivers. It gives me the willies."

"It is rather disconcerting," I agreed, "I suppose it's a type of quirk induced by a childhood inhibition."

She was sarcastic. "Maybe if his parents would evaluate their own influence on the boy instead of criticizing his teachers he'd become a pretty good chap."

To this I could agree. "That's true of most families. We're so busy looking at the disturbing characteristics in other people that our own inhibitions are hidden. Obviously, some of my asinine ways are repulsive to Sam's parents. And, vice versa, they seem off their rocker to me. Yet I'm aware of their family devotion to each other. In many respects, they're a great family with a fine heritage." I paused to bring my mind back to the subject under discussion, "You and I both know," I continued, "this little boy wouldn't keep you out of his school."

She replied seriously, "I suppose I'd come rather than give up teaching but I'm not sure how long I'd last. I know I couldn't do any more for those children than you have done. My present program would never fit in your school. The parents would be disappointed because you've done better work in some phases than I could with the same pupils. As for a championship speller, the idea is preposterous; it takes a long time to make a champion plus a lot of community co-operation. Then, I don't know how I'd ever get across the last ten miles of road when snow started piling up in huge drifts."

She hadn't said anything new, so I invited her into my mud puddle. "Why don't you start looking for another school?"

Her response was enlightening to me. "I suppose the main reason is both of us will be back next year. According to the grapevine, both our followings are getting up a petition to keep us where we are. I'm sure the board will retract its statement.

This was a new wrinkle to me. "I hadn't heard the latest gossip. As for the papa of my special pupil, he knows perfectly well I've done a good job, and if the community opposes his brain storm, he'll jump on their band wagon. He isn't particularly interested in what is being played so long as he's the drum major."

She laughed, "You are so right." "Now it's my turn to ask a question. Are you going to stay here?"

"No, I've considered many angles in this present situation and think it's best for me to go. I want to get established in a large school system, and I suspect this is as good a time as any to make the break."

She didn't argue. "I like a lot of your pupils and I know they want you to stay. My own feeling is this would be reason enough for staying. But you probably would be better off in a large system. As for me, I've enjoyed working with you and who knows what my relationship will be to this school after you're gone."

I smiled, "It'll probably be much better. Anyway,"

I continued, "we can't settle anything now because neither of us has been asked to return." She was right, however. The patrons in both schools objected so strenuously that the newly formed policy was laid on the table for future consideration.

Whether Grandma intended to get rid of me or just ruffle her feathers to usurp more authority, I don't know. One thing was sure, I was tired of battling extracurricular forces. It was bad enough to keep my brood contented without interference from the sidelines. The idea of a new setup with new faces and challenges appealed to me. I'd done a good job and the board's first reaction was three years for a teacher in one school, so I decided to try a greener pasture.

At first the county superintendent was a bit reluctant to have me leave her range. She knew of other schools that offered wonderful opportunities for a teacher with my experience and qualifications. Since I didn't want to find myself out on a limb, I encouraged her to present my name in one of her perfect schools. In the meantime, I looked for greener grass and told her of my dreams. She cooperated a hundred per cent, so it wasn't long before I signed a contract to teach in a large school system. Only time would tell whether this was a wise choice.

Chapter IX

SUMMER JOYS

Before a teacher can leave his four walls of solitary confinement and venture out into the clashing, clanging, greedy, grasping world, he must accomplish about three months work in one. The last month of teacher-pupil combat, if compressed for public exhibition, would draw a larger crowd than the world series.

In a school like mine there was always the last-minute grooming of eighth-grade pupils. Were they ready for high school? What were their weak points, and how could they be corrected at this late hour? Then, as if scholastic achievement were not enough, there was an array of public appearances which demanded speeches, dramatic acting, and music. Because they were graduating from the eighth grade, they were expected to excel in everything.

The patrons in our school expected to see a dramatic production equal to any high school three-act play. This required hours of drill in dramatic arts and music. Naturally, each student had to have a major part in some play or musical production.

How to make a movie star out of a dumb Dora was a question to tax the ingenuity of the saints.

Our school papas enjoyed athletic events, so boys and girls had to be trained in track as well as softball. We held our district olympics on the last day of school. In order to make a creditable showing, time was taken from other subjects to make athletes out of clumsy thirteen- and fourteen-year-old boys. Personally, I have never discovered a recipe that will take the awkwardness out of a growing boy.

Naturally, the kids felt entitled to special consideration, so just prior to the close of my last year a wolf howl was heard demanding a school party. "We've worked hard all year," contended Judy, "so when may we have a party?"

"Hard!" I shouted. "Name one day when you did any kind of work, let alone hard work."

"I can do that," yelled Ted, "we never get recess and only time enough to eat lunch during test week."

"Yes," cried Ruth, "and what about the extra hours we spent getting ready for television."

"How about you, Dick?" I asked. "Did you ever work enough to warrant a party?"

Dick, whose IQ was around one hundred and thirty, gave an innocent, boyish grin and nonchalantly answered, "Oh, I work sometimes but probably not enough to earn a party."

"There," I blurted out, "we have one honest pupil in this school."

As usual, Sharon sealed the discussion. "It's hardly fair to judge the school by my kid brother. Actually, he does some work at home so he can have more leisure time in school.

"It looks as if the odds are against me," I said, "but I warn you there is a test coming up that will cover half a year."

Again Sharon had a solution. "If we took our test a week early, we could get our studies out of the way and have time for other things."

Gordon had shown little interest in our discussion up to this point but now he offered an opinion. "An early test sounds O.K. to me, I vote with Sharon."

"Yeah," shouted a mighty chorus as all hands flew up in the air.

"So be it," I agreed. "We'll take our tests according to your wishes, Vivian." I continued, "You're the president of this motley bunch, so get your committees in action and let me know what you plan to do."

Coupled with parties and tests was the ever present exhibit. Notebook covers were not all made, a few pictures were incomplete, there were articles only half finished, not all the booklets were put together, and a number of picture frames had to be made. The kids all had good intentions, but I knew the hour of reckoning would demand midnight oil burning on my workbench in order to finish what the laggards left undone. Even if the kids were indifferent about certain types of craft work, I knew there papas and mammas expected to see their names on a fine article or picture.

Intermingled with tests, crafts, festivities, plays,

and music were last minute school reports. Since our tests were held early, I was able to get the grade cards completed in fine style and have a margin of time for annual reports. The question of how to get everything done at the appointed hour has been unanswered throughout the years, but somehow teachers manage it and schools continue to thrive.

Once school was out, my next step was to find employment. This is not always easy because thousands of high-school and college boys are doing the same thing. Preferences are often extended to these young fellows because employers contend that teachers have a job and students need money. Of course, one little item is that teachers aren't able to earn enough during nine months of school to last over three summer months. Obviously, therefore, a few extra shekels help supplement the household larder.

One summer I secured employment as a taxi driver, which is probably a good job for some people. The teacher, however, might do well to look elsewhere. A car seat is fine for commuting back and forth to work, but a car seat gets mighty distressing after a daily diet of twelve or thirteen hours. Another little annoyance is people. People are nice in their homes or endurable on the telephone, but waiting for a taxi seems to disturb their sense of chivalry and their anger spills over on the taxi driver. Traffic is a little frustrating to the average motorist, but the taxi driver must make time to make money. All in all, there are more desirable summer occupations for a teacher than driving a taxi. The guy who fights kids, parents, and fellow teachers for nine months doesn't relish doing battle with the teeming masses for the other three months.

I suppose one of the most satisfying jobs for me was employment as a park ranger. This has its disadvantages, particularly if school continues late in the spring and begins early in the fall. A seasonal ranger is needed from approximately the first of June until Labor Day.

I received my appointment as a ranger with a liberal mixture of joy and ignorance. My first shock came in regard to the price of a uniform. Fortunately, today an allowance is made for uniforms, but I had to dig deep in my pockets. My next step was a period of instruction which consisted of listening to speeches that lasted a couple of days. Then work began. Since everything was new to me, I was as dumb as I felt. Fortunately, I stayed in the ranger station with several fellows who knew the ropes. It soon became apparent I was a buck private in the army, at least insofar as general organization was concerned. Orders were given and executed in army style. My job was not to question why. I learned that sometimes the task leads to the brink of death. But no ranger, to my knowledge, during my stay in the park, was ever killed in the line of duty. Our job was to prevent tragedy rather than rescue the perishing. Of course, even in the best regulated families accidents occur.

There were a lot of pleasant days. A ranger friend and I spent our days off hiking in the mountains or driving to scenic spots. We drove along park roads and watched bears beg for food, saw herds of elk in their original habitat, moose crushing vegetation in swampland, deer bounding through the dense forest, and the mighty buffaloes roaming over green pastures. Occasionally we stopped to look at wildlife in the lowlands or what once was an ocean bed. Rugged mountain peaks towered high above our heads, and we gazed in awe at their grandeur. Here and there a frigid glacier reminded us of past periods when huge sheets of ice covered the valley on which smooth highways now afforded rapid transportation. This was the artistry of God with indescribable designs of majesty and beauty.

We hiked on some of the many trails wending their way through deep gorges and over towering mountains. These hikes afforded an opportunity for quiet study and deep appreciation of nature. The unique manner in which God designed a weed to magnify the rich color in a flower, or planted a large bouquet of flowers in an array of varied colors was a mystery for the botanist to unravel rather than a tenderfoot ranger to mull over. My goal was to enjoy God's handiwork.

Here and there a chipmunk broke the silence of the forest with his chatter and a gray squirrel leaped from branch to branch to antagonize two cooing love birds. Marmots lounged on the rocks and little pikas squeaked their merry hello. Pine martens made their home in the attic of our cabin and barked like angry foxes trying to frighten intruders away. These and more were seen in the park and along the trail as we tuned our ears to the music of nature and feasted our eyes on her rich relaxing colors. Jeremiah might have been unable to find balm in Gilead, but the mountains were filled with a healing ointment of immortal peace designed to assuage the troubled soul of man.

Unfortunately, the serpent appeared in God's original Paradise and continues to stick his writhing head above the surface today. Dan, a ranger friend, and I were getting ready for dinner one evening when a loud blast from the fire siren split the air. I jumped up from the table and yelled, "What do we do now, Dan?" This was our first experience with fire fighters.

"I don't know," was Dan's answer, "but I imagine we better hurry over to the fire cache."

We left our food untouched and drove as rapidly as we dared to the fire cache. Here we learned of a forest fire. Already one car had gone to the boat dock with fire-fighting equipment. Our own pickup was quickly loaded with more equipment and we left for the boat dock. In a short time a dozen rangers were going across the lake with hard hats, flashlights, axes, water pump, motor, hoses, fire extinguishers, and even rations. We landed on the shore and pushed back into a densely wooded area. I stumbled over fallen logs and finally came to a marsh. We walked through this and set up our motor on the far side, which was within a hundred yards of a roaring inferno. A couple of us stayed to operate the pump while others stretched out the hose, cut away brush, or used other types of fire-fighting equipment.

It was dusk when we left the cabin and two A.M. when we gathered up our equipment to leave a blackened charcoal area now saturated with water. It had not taken long, because we caught the fire before it engulfed the tree tops. By three o'clock we reached our cabin, cold, wet, and tired. "Dan," I said, "this sort of excitement is a little out of my line."

Dan threw himself on the bed. "I'm completely fagged out." His voice sounded tired. "I've been in an office nine months trying to take care of unruly kids. Now I'm suddenly thrust into a situation that requires seasoned fire fighters. No wonder I'm tired."

I had a teakettle on the stove. "Shall we each drink a cup of coffee to warm our insides, then go to bed, and have our dinner tomorrow?"

"That suits me," he groaned, "I'm too tired to eat."

In a few minutes I had our coffee made. We were tired, but the coffee never tasted better. I put the dirty cups in the sink and was asleep almost before my head hit the pillow. Strenuous fire fighting for teachers was a little early in the season. We needed a couple of months of mountain climbing to toughen up for the this type of work.

Not long after the fire escapade I wore blisters on my feet looking for a mother and her teen-age daughter. Once more it was dusk when the report came of lost women. A ranger and I tramped through the woods until about midnight, then came back for more help. Bolstered by added help, we again went out, walking and shouting. After an especially loud blast, a seasoned ranger said, "Listen." I cocked my ear but only the forest sounds came to me. He listened a moment longer and said, "Come this way."

We followed him at a fast pace and came upon a piece of paper, then another, then another. Obviously, the women had decided to mark their trail. Now we were on the right path, so in another fifteen minutes the mother and daughter were found near a pile of pine needles. They were sparsely clad and had covered themselves wtih pine needles to shield themselves from the cold mountain air. Although this was our job, we won some very gracious friends.

One morning the telphone rang and the district ranger said there was a car wreck about ten miles down the road. Would I go with the patrolman to investigate? Nothing was known about the wreck, so we opened the siren, turned on the red light, and stepped on the gas. Traveling at a high rate of speed in the park is very dangerous even for a patrol car, so we were happy to arrive safe and sound. The patrolman quickly put two people in his ambulance and went to the hosiptal. I checked on the wreck. I measured distances, took testimonies, and finally cleared the highway. Both families were sent on their way, and the case was closed for me. Who was to blame? It's difficult to say. One car was driving at a snail's pace in order to enjoy the mountains. Another car came up quite rapidly, also looking at the mountains. When the driver realized how rapidly she was approaching the slow car, it was too late to stop. She could not go around because of an approaching automobile, so she slammed on her brakes and took the bump as lightly as possible. This is how it happens quite often in the park.

Tourists, although on vacation, are not always in the best humor when things don't go to their liking. Consider, for example, the fellow who quarreled with his boss over the time of his vacation, quarreled with his wife about what to take and where to go, drove six hundred miles on a hot sultry day to get there, took time out to paddle three kids along the way, listened to the baby's incessant howling most of the way, and arrived at the campground about dusk to demand a campsite. As usual, we always filled up about noon, so when this fellow arrived with his customary demand I had no alternative except point to the sign which says, "Campground Full," and give directions on how to reach another location.

His anger held long enough to say, "I've driven six hundred miles today, the kids are tired and cranky, and the baby needs to rest. We just need a place big enough to park the car."

Very patiently I explained, "This campground is designed with individual sites. When you pull in one of the sites, it is yours and no other campers are allowed to pull in with you. The sites were all filled before noon. Fortunately, however, we have an overflow where you can spend the night; then, if you desire, you can return here in the morning and find a site that will be yours."

Now came the explosion, cursing, shouting, and threatening. "I paid money to get in this park and by—I want a place to park."

Once more I very calmly but firmly explained, "Our park regulations were made for the comfort of people like you—people who need a place to rest, but you cannot rest with a lot of other families shoving at your elbow; for that reason these sites are available on the first-come first-serve basis. You may come in the morning and find a site, but we have nothing available except the overflow tonight." This particular man cooled off and accepted what we had to offer but a few individuals threaten to see the district ranger or write to Washington. In fact, a few letters are written to either Washington or our own park headquarters. They have no effect upon the rangers, however, because generally rangers are pretty well-balanced fellows and bend over backward to help the tourists.

An example of their behavior is evidenced in an event that took place at the girl's dormitory. Our telephone rang about three A.M. asking for all of us to come to the dormitory. Four young fellows had tanked up on beer and went into the girls' dorm. The girls locked themselves in their rooms and yelled for help. The manager called a ranger, and he called us so we arrived for battle.

When the fellows were questioned, they refused to give their names or place of employment. They were very indignant even after the arrival of the district ranger. It became necessary to put them in the patrol car and take them to jail, where they later stood trial. Keeping peace in the park often takes courage as well as patience. These fellows were a rough element who refrained from attacking the rangers only because they feared defeat.

Courage is exhibited every summer by rangers who climb mountains to rescue individuals or parties who become lost in a storm, are hit by a rock, slipped off a precipice, or in some other manner suffered bone fracture or death.

Sometimes parties are out on the lake when high winds arise. I was out on patrol one day with another ranger checking on possible isolated small boats because the wind was rising to a point of danger. Before we could reach shore, a sixty-five-mile-an-hour gust came upon our patrol boat, and we scarcely made it to shore. A smaller boat would have gone to the bottom. Less than three weeks earlier a fisherman was caught in a similar gale and he failed to make shore. His body was found floating near a clump of weeds.

Thus the ranger is privileged to have a part in the joys and tragedies of life. After three months in the mountain passes, mingling with thousands of people, it is good to return to the stable, uneventful tasks of teaching. No, not uneventful, for although the joys and experiences of a ranger are many, they do not exceed the privileges and blessings of a teacher.

CHAPTER X

BROADER HORIZONS

The advantages of a large school system come at a price. I realize that the East or Far West has much larger and more complicated systems, but for the wide-open spaces my new setup was like climbing out of a small pond into a huge lake. Whereas once, to a large degree, I could determine my own procedure, now I jumped at the crack of an executive bullwhip.

A letter came to the national park informing me of an institute that would be held prior to the opening of school. My special program marked the sessions I was expected to attend. With the county superintendent I might have argued the wisdom of leaving the park before Labor Day in order to waste eight or nine hours listening to some antiquated teacher elaborate on her pet hobby or type of class instruction. In a larger system, however, you don't tell the bull of the woods, "I do not choose to attend." You quietly bow to the inevitable and head toward the induction center.

It was quite an affair, this first meeting in our district. I entered through the huge glass doors of a new high school building that spread over a city block. Near the entrance there were coffee and goodies to delight the taste. A buxom lady, with furrowed brow and streaks of gray in her hair, took me under her wing filled my plate with sweets, introduced me to several distinguished executives, and left me under the watchful eye of a boisterous athletic coach. Maybe she thought his verbosity would add some exuberance to my reserved shell of self-defense.

The athlete didn't disturb me much, and I was pleased at the large number of handsome young men and beautiful women. This was quite a contrast to the aging damsels with whom I had a former working acquaintanceship. If for no other reason, I had found a just cause for changing schools. Now I was stimulated by the buoyancy of youth rather than exasperated by the dilatoriness of antiquity.

Sometimes a poor play can be endured if produced in an attractive setting . This was true of the speeches given at this affair. For some reason, they seemed less boring when interspersed with occasional glances at the scenic benches around me.

One note was evident in all the speeches that seemed to be more pronounced than was customary. Everyone assured us lessor mentalitics that they were here to co-operate, not dictate, to help, not hinder, to supplement, not deter, and to conform, not transform, our efforts. In many respects this was a new approach to teacher solidarity and achievement. Time would reveal their sincerity.

One of the most impressive phases of the institute was an introductory dinner. I put on my best bib and tucker and took my fattest billfold, expecting the price to knock out my eyeballs and snatch away my appetite. If dress was indicative of the standard of this dinner, it was a swanky affair. Our pretty teachers had been transformed into movie stars, and even the men maintained a debonair attitude. As for me, I reached in my billfold to count my money once more.

Five hundred teachers edged their way into a spacious dining hall and waited for the money-changer. Then quietly the superintendent arose to his feet, cleared his throat, and said, "This meal is on the house." I practically swooned. He then explained it was a good-will gesture and welcome that the district extended to all the teachers. Needless to stay, I was sold on this district. For once somebody was giving me something instead of asking for a handout. I'd come into this district with fear and trembling, but now, by the great horned spoon, I'd stay forever.

My decision was stamped with an immortal seal before the meeting was over. We were served a bounteous meal that fairly melted in our mouths. All free, or was it? Out of the corner of my eye I saw the superintendent rise to his feet. Now the speeches would begin. I twisted in my chair, trying to figure out how to endure the afternoon. A free meal was fine, but now came the payoff. An endurance test— my hip bones against a steady stream of chatter.

The superintendent introduced a long line of dignitaries with enough humor sandwiched in between to make this phase of the program endurable. Then came a long introduction of the school board president. Naturally he would have to have his say. Fortunately, he had been ill and didn't feel equal to a long speech, so I felt a sense of relief. The superintendent rose again, thanked the president, thanked us for coming, wished us the best in our work, reassued us of his full co-operation, and said, "You are adjourned." Was I floored? Obviously this man will have to do a lot of mean things to lose my loyalty.

The next item on my agenda was to visit my new school and satisfy my curiosity about the verbal pictures I'd been given regarding its beautiful location. Thus far I had never visited the school in which I expected to spend the next nine months. Scraps of information indicated that this was a two-teacher school but several families had moved away so I would have only eight pupils and five grades. There were no children in the first, second, and seventh grades. This didn't sound too bad. The only disparaging feature was its distance from civilization. The school was somewhere in the mountains, but no one seemed to know exactly how to get there.

I eventually learned its approximate location, so my wife and I set out on what might well become a sightseeing tour. We understood you could reach the school by way of a mountain road. I had just spent three months in the mountains, so I looked forward to traveling a new trail, and trail it was.

Anyone who has ever driven mountain roads can visualize our trip.

We had the usual steep grades, hairpin curves, narrow bridges, chuckholes, and gravel. Some canyons were lovely. There were broad valleys and flower-covered hillsides. The tall stately pines were as majestic here as in any park area. Then came the peak with its huge boulders and rugged walls. Like all other mountain drives, this was time-consuming because of sharp curves and steep hills. As we came down the mountain, however, and looked out over the valley, there was beauty far exceeding the touch of an artist's brush. Already some fields had been mowed and haystacks decked the valley. Fat cattle grazed lazily in the pasture, giving our picture a tinge of red. A river wended its way as far as the eye could see and nurtured giant trees to break the monotony of flat space. It was a thrill to drive down one mountainside and look across to another with its deep canyons and sharp crevasses. We had scarcely reached the bottom when a huge bird obstructed our pathway. A bald eagle had stopped in the highway to enjoy his midday meal. This was truly a natural paradise, still untamed by the hand of man.

It was only a couple of miles from the eagle's dining room to my school—a lovely light-green building nestling under the protection of gentle hills boring into the heart of a giant fortress of huge granite boulders that towered high in the heavens. Only fifty feet away from the schoolhouse was a rustic log cabin which was to be my home. Just outside the cabin I could park my car in a new pea-green garage. For fear that prowlers might disturb the tranquility of my slumbers, an automatic street light stood between the cabin and the schoolhouse. This came on as dusk crept over the valley. The new building was modern and even lined on the inside with knotty pine.

One obvious difference in this school and my other one was the architecture. This building was evidently designed by a school architect interested in teacher needs rather than a school board concerned about tax reduction. Chalkboard, bulletin boards, cupboards, kitchen, restrooms, and many other needs were all in their proper place. Lighting came from the southwest, which was right in this area, but daylight was supplemented with long fluorescent lights that gave the room a feeling of warmth and good cheer. This was my equipment; now, what about the pupils? I'd know in a couple of days.

Monday morning the sun came up in all its radiance as is usual, particularly in the early fall. I was waiting at the door when everybody arrived at once. I knew each family provided individual transportation, and I didn't expect them all at the same time.

We exchanged greetings, introduced each to the other, decided upon a few necessary matters, and they left. I went into the schoolhouse to count noses. Instead of five grades, I had eleven pupils and eight grades. Why these mammas had to hatch their young 'uns in just this order, I'll never know. Well, maybe it wouldn't matter too much. There were so many hours in a day, and I expected to be busy whether I taught five grades or eight.

These kids were very much like all others in their age bracket. They sat like little cherubs in the seats designated to them. I made no effort to release their tension. Why break the spell until necessary? We managed to find enough books for each class, so work began. There were no geniuses to embarrass me with their display of wisdom by illuminating my stupidity. In fact, this seemed like a very average school with normal students. Naturally, they were curious about the peculiar antics of their teacher, but since I didn't throw any tantrums, they pegged me as an ordinary screwball type of instructor and settled own to work.

I noticed a few differences in some phase of procedure in this school that varied slightly from those of my past experience. For example, in this school the parents were asked to take out insurance for their children. This not only protected the parents for a nominal fee but the district was free of condemnation in the event of an accident. Here a flat fee was charged for books, which enabled the district to provide suitable material yet gave the boys and girls a feeling of possession. With some pupils this meant greater concern for the care of their books, whereas others went on the basis, "I paid for them so I can do as I damn please." My own reaction tended to lean favorably toward the system, particularly for this community. Another thing, certain phases of schoolwork were supplemented by professional instructors.

From the teacher's standpoint this added help was a panacea. Art and music teachers came regularly once a month. They brought material for work and utilized the entire day. It always proved a gala affair, because it digressed from our routine method of study. As a teacher, all I had to do was observe and see that the kids carried out their assignments for that month. If I needed more material, or wanted to pursue a certain line of study, I simply told the instructors what I hoped to accomplish. To some degree, this type of instruction sort of passed the buck. They could say, "The teacher didn't carry out our assignments." On the other hand, I could say, "The instructors didn't leave any work to be done, so the pupils studied only when they came." It is conceivable that this could be done, but my experience was just the reverse. Their efforts lightened my load and heightened my goals.

Other teachers, nurses, surpervisors, and even carpenters came throughout the year. If a job needed to be done that was not my direct responsibility, all I did was notify the authorities and someone would come to do it.

One day I said to the co-ordinator, "Two things need some attention in this school."

"Only two!" she exclaimed. "If there are only two I should be able to do something about at least one of them."

I wasn't used to a dignitary solving my problems,

so I hesitated before diving in this mud puddle; then I decided to take the plunge. "First of all, I'm not sure I'm doing a good job with these little first- and second-grade girls. Second, I need a number of things, such as paper, pencils, erasers, and other articles."

She didn't utter a word but said, "I'll be out in two days to check your girls and order whatever you need."

Two days later she held classes with all my students and gave me an encouraging boost. When we sat down to order my material, she always added a little more than I suggested. Truly, my supervisors were here to help, not hinder. In less than a day I learned to appreciate some of the merits of a consolidated school. It was not just co-operative supervisors who added strength to such a system but the wide variety of specialists ready to assist any teacher who needed assistance. A teacher felt secure, adequate, and big. He was not just a knot on a log but part of a great organization doing a noble work for thousands of boys and girls.

I was curious to know how the community reacted to this venture in which small schools were under the jurisdiction of a centralized government instead of district controlled. Although Money Bags, the man I approached, had no children in school, he was definitely interested in what was going on in the community. I never learned how much of the valley he owned, but he ran eight hundred breeding cows in an area where thirty acres were needed to pasture one cow. For the novice I might explain that cattle were pastured in three different sections. Early in the spring they grazed in the lowlands and sagebrush. Later in the summer they were taken to the mountains. Finally, as midsummer approached, they were moved back across to the other side of the valley. Such maneuvering required considerable space for a herd of cattle.

In our conversation about cattle I worked around to asking Money Bags, "How do you like your type of school consolidation?"

"I opposed it at first," he said, "but there are some definite advantages."

"Are the advantages worth the price?" I asked.

He looked at me quizzically, "My taxes went up sixty per cent."

"Sixty per cent!" I exclaimed, "that seems impossible."

His attitude indicated this huge jump had a lot of ramifications not evident in a cold, untarnished statement. "We were running this district on an uncommonly low budget," he explained. "Take, for example, our water. A ranchman furnished the spring and several of us piped the water into our old schoolhouse. We also did without a lot of modern conveniences; also, our teachers weren't paid as much as teachers in the city schools. The sixty per cent is really not a true picture, but we did suffer a big jump."

I looked at the new building. "It looks as if you got a new schoolhouse along with other advantages."

"Yes," he said, "we didn't have to do a thing toward this new building. The building and its upkeep is all a part of our over-all plan." He paused a moment as if in deep thought. "I suppose our greatest advantage is in the realm of instructors. We get the same quality teachers as those in our city schools. Then we have the added services of their specialists. It all adds up to quite a bit. I'm glad we voted to unite."

"You get some financial aid for student transportation, don't you?" I asked.

His face lighted up, "That's another benefit we didn't allow under the old system. Today each family is paid to bring their children to school and a reasonable allowance is made for high school transportation."

I smiled, "Living on a ranch back in the hills is almost like living in the city today, isn't it?"

"It sure is," he admitted, "if we refuse to move to the city the city will move out to us." He was right. We had reached an era when the individual was becoming more and more a part of his social surroundings. The wide open spaces were rapidly receding into the milling hordes of restless mankind. Whether this is good or bad may be conjecture, but the ultimate is obvious—you can only impede, not stop progress.

Certain Indian tribes rebelled against the encroaching white man, but civilization continued to creep forward, and no force could stop it. The ways of the pioneer must inevitably give way to new concepts and these concepts will yield to future theories of progress until they too fade with the passing of time.

Centuries have proved that man's philosophies are immortal only to the extent that they dovetail with infinity. Man can unfold theories of conduct and behavior that exceed those of his forefathers, such as modes of travel, medication, and even more efficient methods of accumulating facts, but these all give way to advanced ideas as each generation attempts to sprout its wings.

The Indian with his type of social life gave way to the white man and his unique concept of civilization. Likewise, an antiquated school system may stem the tide for a few years but progress demands ultimate conformity. The pioneer district of yesterday cannot long stand against engulfing efficiencies of today. Schoolteaching is a great professson, but we teachers, like the car manufacturers who each year advertize better and more efficient cars, need to be constantly alert to new and more advanced methods for the enrichment of young minds waiting to be molded by our stupidity or wisdom. Stupidity if we teach only for today, but wisdom if we teach for eternity.

Many years ago a kindhearted teacher came along and said, "The heart of the universe is love." Or, in simpler terms, "God is love." Men have attempted to disprove this statement through force, economics, biology, psychology, and other forms of thought but always each succeeding generation reverts back to this one simple fact, "God is love." This teacher found the key to the heart of the universe. Other keys may unlock various chambers leading to the heart, but only love opens the secret door that leads to eternal life. If our teaching is centered in love, it will last throughout the aeons.